Bernard Finster
Aug. 1961

## STATEMENT CONCERNING PUBLICATIONS
## OF RUSSELL SAGE FOUNDATION

*Russell Sage Foundation was established in 1907 by Mrs. Russell Sage "for the improvement of social and living conditions in the United States of America." While the general responsibility for management of the Foundation is vested in the Board of Trustees, the responsibility for facts, conclusions, and interpretations in its publications rests with the authors and not upon the Foundation, its Trustees, or its staff. Publication under the imprint of the Foundation does not imply agreement by the organization with all opinions or interpretations expressed. It does imply that care has been taken that the work on which a manuscript is based has been thoroughly done.*

# PATIENTS' VIEWS
## of
# MEDICAL PRACTICE

### —A Study of Subscribers to a Prepaid Medical Plan in The Bronx

*By*

**ELIOT FREIDSON**

New York University

*and*

Montefiore Hospital

# RUSSELL SAGE FOUNDATION
New York                                      1961

# Contents

3

## Part Two

## The Utilization of Health Services

## Part Three

## Images for the Study of Medical Care

# Tables

6

# Acknowledgments

THIS BOOK IS ITSELF a token acknowledgment of the profound debt I owe my parents. I can acknowledge other debts more simply.

I owe Russell Sage Foundation thanks for financial support during the first year of the study I report here, and for publishing this book. Drs. Donald Young, Esther Lucile Brown, and Leonard S. Cottrell, Jr., all of the Foundation, have shown me many kindnesses for which I am grateful.

I owe thanks to the Division of Social Medicine of Montefiore Hospital for its financial support during the years succeeding my Russell Sage Foundation residency. Dr. Martin Cherkasky, director of Montefiore Hospital, and Dr. George A. Silver, chief of the Division of Social Medicine, created an unusually free and stimulating context in which to do research, think, and write.

Thanks are due Abraham B. Siegelaub and Edith Pais for their aid in processing the statistical material of this study, Joseph Axelrod and Alice White for smoothing away administrative problems, and Helen Schulman for indefatigable secretarial assistance.

Permission by the Society for Applied Anthropology, the University of Chicago Press, and the American Public Health Association to reprint here portions of my articles in *Human Organization*, the *American Journal of Sociology*, and the *American Journal of Public Health* is gratefully acknowledged.

My many intellectual debts are in part acknowledged by reference in the text. Some, however, deserve special mention. I owe much to my former teachers at the University of Chicago— Everett C. Hughes, the late Robert Redfield, and W. Lloyd Warner (now at Michigan State University). Each in his own way represents what is best in sociology: determination to grapple in close with reality without illusion, sufficient imagination to wrench order out of the glut of human affairs, a steady sense of humanity.

Finally, I owe much to those who read my manuscript in draft. It is impossible for anyone who has not himself tried the appalling task of writing a book to know how enormously helpful are colleagues who take the time and trouble to read a manuscript critically. My wife, Marion Freidson, and Howard S. Becker and George A. Silver patiently read a number of drafts of various chapters, each time pointing out deficiencies and suggesting improvements. Robert Bierstedt, Joel R. Davitz, Sylvia Gilliam, Edward Wellin, and Harold L. Wilensky made helpful comments on the penultimate draft. The aid of these valued colleagues corrected many deficiencies which might otherwise have been overlooked. Whatever deficiencies remain are my own.

E. F.

# Introduction

MEDICAL PRACTICE, like any other form of applied knowledge, requires for its very existence satisfaction of conditions that lie outside its domain of technical expertness. This may be seen when we think of the process by which medical knowledge is applied. First, the prospective patient, a layman, must decide that he needs help. Second, he must decide that he needs help from a physician and not a lawyer, banker, priest. Third, he must find a physician or medical service that is available to him. Fourth, he must cooperate with the examination and history-taking. Fifth, his difficulty must be diagnosed and proper treatment prescribed, or if this cannot be done he must be persuaded to see a physician who can diagnose his condition and prescribe proper treatment. Sixth, he must carry out or cooperate with the prescribed treatment.

Patently, only in the fifth step is purely medical, technical capacity involved. That capacity cannot be exercised without fulfillment of prior steps which do not rest upon medical science at all. And even if that capacity could be exercised without its prior conditions, it would be a purely academic exercise if the patient failed to follow its dictates. The basic conditions for medical practice are sociological in character. The basic problem of practice is to fulfill those sociological conditions—to get the patient to report for a medical examination and to gain his co-operation in treatment. However, it is not a problem of *either* the patient or the doctor but of *both*. A system of relationships is involved, and participating in the system are organized institutions as well as individual knowledge and attitudes.

Most recent studies in the field of medical care either have not dealt with a system of relationships at all, or have dealt with only portions of that system. Indeed, most have shared a limited preoccupation with what it is about the patients themselves, and even more particularly, what it is about the attitudes and knowledge of patients, that is responsible for their desirable or undesirable behavior. Patient behavior is not seen as a response to a definite system of medical practice so much as a product of the characteristics of the patient as such. The burden falls on the patient, his behavior being a function of his inadequate knowledge, his foreign culture, or his emotional imbalance. The findings determined by this view suggest that the solution to the problem of getting the patient to consult the doctor is both to change the patient's attitudes and increase his store of knowledge and, by including more knowledge about the patient in formal medical education, to influence the physician to be somewhat more tolerant and flexible about patients' behavior.

More than education, emotional maturity and good intentions are involved, however. The doctor and patient each has a distinct perspective that contradicts the other's. Each is at least potentially constrained and limited by a social structure that is fairly independent of his individual sophistication. A physician with little available time who is confronted by dozens of patients all demanding and needing his services at once, simply is not able, with the best intelligence and good will, to treat each patient as a "whole."[1] And on his side, a patient who "knows" the right way to behave cannot put that knowledge into effect by seeing a doctor if the doctor is too busy, if his fees are too high, or if he is too far away.

Somewhat less obvious, but of at least as great importance, is the variable of organization. The way a task is organized affects the way it can be performed independently of the intent or skill of the performer; the way medical practice is organized affects the way medicine is likely to be applied. Purely solo practice is likely to encourage a doctor to work one way, while hospital or clinic practice is likely to encourage him to work another way. As we shall see later on in this book, the organization of the potential patient's community life is likely to mold his responses

[1] Bryner, Ulrich R., "Auxiliary Services" in *The Physician and His Practice*, edited by Joseph Garland. Little, Brown and Co., Boston, 1954, p. 187.

to the doctor, as is the way the organization of practice meshes with the organization of community life.

The assumption that significance must be assigned to the structure as well as the culture of medicine and of patient life flows from knowledge about other areas of human behavior gathered by sociologists and social anthropologists. Social structure is a significant consideration in understanding the family, the factory, and the government agency, and is equally so in medicine. There is much unresolved controversy over the effects of different structural contexts on the practice of medicine. One point of view holds, for example, that the solitary physician working for a fee is more likely to take pains with his patients than a salaried physician. Others argue that, income being assured, the salaried physician in an organization is free of money worries and is therefore able to concentrate on "good" medicine. On these issues there is much debate and little systematic, empirical evidence.

## Background of the Study

This book will report a rather modest empirical study that explored the attitudes and behavior of patients who have had experience with more than one way of organizing medical practice, and thereby sought to suggest some of the ways in which both lay and professional social structure figure in the utilization of medical care. The data are used to derive a tentative conceptual framework that takes account of structural as well as cultural factors in understanding the behavior of doctors and patients. The net result is a set of ideas that suggest the nature of the medical system that lies outside the walls of hospitals, in direct contact with the community.

I had occasion to make the study when in the fall of 1955, through the generosity of Russell Sage Foundation, I was appointed social science resident in the Family Health Maintenance Demonstration. The Family Health Maintenance Demonstration was an important venture in experimenting with a new method of offering medical care to Americans. Supported by a variety of sources, it was operated within the Montefiore Medical Group.

Social structure as such was not my original concern upon entering the Demonstration. Rather, it grew as I sought to make sense of data collected on patient and professional behavior. As social science resident I was there to learn something about medical care and was free to study what I chose so long as it did not interfere with the daily operation of the Demonstration or the Medical Group. After observing the work of the staff in a variety of situations for three or four months I became convinced that the performance of the staff could not be understood very clearly without reference to the expectations of the patients. So I spent a few months visiting patients in their homes and interviewing them as extensively and intensively as possible. Initial analysis of these interviews led to the formulation of a questionnaire administered by mail which was focused on patient perception of the roles of the Family Health Maintenance Demonstration staff.

Analysis of these data led me to feel that the patients' perception of the roles of the Demonstration staff was a function not only of the organization of staff work as such and of the patients' stereotypes about one professional role or another, but also of the way the patients determined and defined the problems they brought to the Demonstration for help. The process of perceiving the need for help and then seeking it often seemed to involve a pattern of events, a sequence of steps. The sequence could be expressed by reference to the kind of person, lay or professional, consulted by the patient at each stage of his search for help. In this sense the sequence could be conceived as a structure of consultant statuses through which the patient moves on his way to specific medical or professional services.

By the nature of the case, however, choice and other aspects of patient behavior could not be fully comprehended without reference to the alternatives that confronted the patient and the relation of those alternatives to his demands and expectations. So it was necessary to reexamine the organization of the professional services chosen or rejected by the patients, and the way in which that organization did or did not mesh into the lay structure of seeking help. In the development of my study, then, staff functions were examined first, only to find that to understand them patients had to be studied, too. The study of patients led back to staff functions and the organization of professional practice, only this time from a new angle—the way they linked in with the lay organization of patient behavior. The conceptual image thus came to be one involving two major structures, the lay and the professional, in interaction, meshing at some points and failing to mesh, or clashing at others.

## The Nature of the Study Situation

The situation studied seemed unusually well designed to reveal the significance of social structure in the use of medical care. For one thing, it allowed a comparative point of view. In most circumstances one has the opportunity to study patients confronted by only one sort of medical care program. Under those circumstances one studies variable patient behavior in the face of a constant medical practice and, since it is difficult to determine what part of patient behavior is a function of the structure of services, attention becomes focused instead on attributes of the patients that are associated with variations in behavior even though it is patent that the nature of practice forms some kind of limiting condition to patient behavior. In the situation studied the patients were constant and the structure of medical services was variable. The central core of patients studied had experience with three different ways of organizing medical care—the Family Health Maintenance Demonstration, in which everyday treatment was given by an interprofessional team working in a prepaid, centralized medical group; the Montefiore Medical Group, in which everyday care was provided by individual pediatricians and internists who worked within the framework of a prepaid, centralized medical group; and conventional solo, fee-for-service practice, in which everyday care was provided by individual practitioners working in their own scattered offices. More information about the patients and the practices will be provided in Chapter 1. Here it is sufficient to note that the variety allowed focus on structural differences between practices. When patients chose to use one practice rather than another, it was possible to illuminate their choice by reference to the way in which the structure of the chosen practice fitted into the structure of patient life.

The opportunity for comparison was probably the most important single characteristic of the situation studied, but two more characteristics should be mentioned. For one thing, unlike most situations in the United States, the problem of money was here in large part controlled. All the patients were subscribers to a medical care plan under the terms of which they were entitled to fairly extensive medical services. Once subscribers by virtue of paying their premiums, they could at least theoretically use the generalists, specialists, and laboratory facilities of the plan for an unlimited number of times during the year without having to pay additional fees. Thus, while the personal income of the subscribers varied greatly, utilization of services was potentially independent of income. This allowed fairly realistic concentration upon other than economic variables in the use of medical care.

Finally, while it may be obvious it is nonetheless important to point out that unlike many others, the situation studied was one in which the normal routine of everyday patient behavior could be examined closely. Far too many studies have been based on examination of overspecialized and "abnormal" situations. Bed patients in hospitals are unusually helpless by virtue of their illness. Patients in outpatient departments and public or quasi-public clinics are under unusual constraint by virtue of their supplicant or underprivileged status. The patients studied in this survey are certainly, like those in hospitals and outpatient departments, a captive population, all being enrolled in a particular insurance plan and visiting a single centralized medical group. But like the bulk of "normal" patients everywhere, they are most often not so sick as to be desperate, and, since they are "paying" patients, they are in a position to seek to control their own destinies. They can be as troublesome or as cooperative as "normal" patients who are not members of a captive population, and so I was in a position to learn from them what is the everyday reality of seeking medical care.

## The Nature of the Data

The data reported here stem from a variety of sources. One important source is a series of questionnaires all administered by mail. Three questionnaires were administered to both husbands and wives of the Family Health Maintenance Demonstration families, with 85 per cent, 92 per cent, and 81 per cent returns, respectively, from the first questionnaire (administered while the program was still in operation) to the last (a followup questionnaire administered after all patients had been discharged from the program). There was no discernible bias in the pattern of returns from these Demonstration families.

In addition, a fourth questionnaire was administered by mail to a random 10 per cent sample of Health Insurance Plan subscribers who were being served by the Montefiore Medical Group.[1] Of the roughly one thousand people in the sample, 67 per cent returned usable questionnaires. Known bias in the pattern of returns lay in an 8 per cent overrepresentation of female subscribers, a 5 per cent overrepresentation of subscribers between the ages of twenty-nine and forty-five, and a 10 per cent overrepresentation of those subscribers whose contracts cover medical services for their whole family. Copies of all questionnaires appear in the Appendix.

A second important source of data was a series of intensive interviews. The homes of 36 families were visited, and in most cases both husband and wife were interviewed—usually together but sometimes separately. Interviews lasting an average of an hour, but sometimes running over two hours, were thus obtained from 71 subscribers. Of these, 53 were members of families that were being served by the Family Health Maintenance Demonstration. About half of the families were served by one of the two "teams" of Demonstration practitioners; the other half were served by the other "team." All the families had at least three years' experience with the Demonstration. The remaining 18 persons interviewed were adult members of families that had not had contact with the Family Health Maintenance Demonstra-

[1] I wish to thank Paul Densen and Sam Shapiro for drawing the sample of subscribers.

tion, having been served instead by the individual practitioners of the Montefiore Medical Group. All patients who were interviewed, then, had had experience with at least two types of medical care, the Medical Group and "private" practice. The interviews explored their attitudes toward these modes of organizing care, and in particular collected concrete case histories of the events surrounding critical experiences with medical care, and case histories of the way in which chronic ailments, such as allergies and migraine headaches, came to receive treatment.

Finally, valuable insight was obtained from observation of patients and professional workers in the waiting-rooms and corridors of the Medical Group, informal and formal interviews with both Demonstration and Medical Group professional workers, and observation of staff meetings as well as staff-patient conferences. The fairly extensive records—medical, nursing, and social work—could be consulted on particular occasions when questions of fact and of professional judgment arose. More importantly, though, intensive reading of those records provided insight into the professional's view of the nature of the routine administration of health services.

## The Sociology of Occupations

The results of this study have been of some practical value to those concerned with administering the particular medical programs involved, and with planning similar programs for the future. There is little doubt that they are also likely to be at least suggestive to those concerned with other kinds of medical programs. But it was not preoccupation with immediate practical problems that either motivated the study or guided its report. Rather, the motive was to explore facets of reality that could illuminate something of the structure of professional practice and the way the practitioner and the client figure in it. The motive was more to refine, clarify, and contribute some ideas to the sociology of occupations than to address the concrete problem of successful administration of a medical program. And it was this motive that led to the holistic study reported here, for it became clear very early in the investigation that present sociological concepts of professional practice and client-professional relations were painfully inadequate. The first order of business was seen to lie in gathering material to feed the process of induction rather than in deducing hypotheses from what already existed. What is presented, therefore, is in part organized description of the data gathered and in part tentative generalizations made on the basis of those data. In this sense, the report is exploratory—it constitutes a tentative construction of concepts and hypotheses, not proof of an *a priori* set of hypotheses.

The concepts presented revolve around the central problem of defining, classifying, and analyzing the nature of occupations— that term by which we designate the routine, gainful performance of work. In particular, attention will be focused on a kind of work that is becoming of critical and troubling significance to the destiny of modern society—"those kinds of work which consist in doing something for, or to, people."[1] Medicine, of course, is a good example of such work.

I am ultimately concerned with defining and classifying the relationship between client and practitioner by reference to the variable position of each in community and occupational structures. In this sense the aim is to suggest a taxonomy of clients and of practices which might conceivably be useful as a trial classification of personal service occupations in general. What I have done is predicated on the assumption "that [in work] there is some struggle of wills or of consciences or both over the level of effort and of product,"[2] and therefore that the direction of resolution of that struggle is critical to the fate of the practitioner, his work, and his client. Professional practice comes to be defined by (1) the way it obtains a clientele, and (2) the amount of control it can exercise over the behavior of its clientele, the two being rather closely related.

One thing should be clear about the empirical source of these definitions. The major source of data used here was the patient.

[1] Hughes, Everett C., *Men and Their Work*. The Free Press, Glencoe, Ill., 1958, p. 69.
[2] *Idem*, "The Sociological Study of Work: An Editorial Foreword," *American Journal of Sociology*, vol. 57, March, 1952, p. 426.

While I have not ignored other investigators' studies of professional practitioners, and while I myself gathered some data directly from practitioners, I have nonetheless worked largely with data *about* professional practice that were provided by patients. It is as though I studied a business firm largely through the eyes of its customers. If we are to take seriously Simon's inclusion of the customer in the roles of the business firm,[1] however, and if we remember that the client is a major contingency in any service occupation, this perspective, while partial and limited, obviously has something to teach us.

### Theory in an Applied Setting

In attempting to make a contribution to theory through research in an applied setting, there are several disturbing problems. On the whole, sociological analysis most commonly takes place in the course of examining points of strain or crisis, not by rounded description of reality. This procedure, while it illuminates much of importance, tends by the sheer intensity of its focus to give a falsely negative look to the subject of the study. And when the analytical point of view is largely restricted to only one kind of concept, the danger of distortion is even greater.

There is little doubt that ultimate explanation of problems of applied medicine lies in the examination of more than one level of reality. Undoubtedly, there is ground for a psychology or psychiatry of patient and of professional behavior. There is also ground for examination of the norms, culture, or "knowledge" involved in the behavior of each, and for examination of the social organization of the behavior of each. Each of these is a roughly separate level of analysis, each is valid, and each is partial. Theoretically, all three should be dealt with concurrently, but attempts to do so tend to flounder in a mire of diffuseness. It is for this reason that I have chosen to ignore almost entirely the psychological level of analysis. While I could not ignore it altogether, I have minimized the normative or cultural level of

[1] Simon, Herbert, *Administrative Behavior*. Macmillan Co., New York, 1958, pp. 16–18.

analysis. By concentrating on the structural level I hope not only to emphasize something that has not received the attention in medical sociology that it deserves, but also to avoid the confusion of a more eclectic approach. What this concentration may gain in clarity, however, it risks losing by distortion. The risk may be attenuated somewhat by specifying the nature of the distortion so that it may be taken into account in evaluating the results.

Structural analysis deals with constraints. Such personal characteristics as spontaneity and creativity, perceptiveness and honesty are seen either as consequences of the analytical variable itself, or as irrelevant to an analysis that holds such variables equal. What are stressed are boundaries to possible behavior. As Selznick put it, "Attention being focused on the structural conditions which influence behavior, we are directed to emphasize constraints, the limitations of alternatives imposed by the system upon its participants. This will tend to give pessimistic overtones to the analysis, since such factors as good will and intelligence will be deemphasized. As a consequence of the central status of constraint, tension and dilemmas will be highlighted."[1] Differences that bear on behavior independently of social structure— differences between the conscientious and the slovenly doctor, the cooperative and intelligent, and the resistant and ignorant patient—will be largely ignored. This obviously influences the shape and sense of the discussion.

An attempt has been made to control this distortion by organizing the report in such a way that insofar as possible there is visible separation between the data and the analysis. Only by presenting raw data can the selective organizing effects of a viewpoint be eliminated entirely, but by using an inductive mode of presentation—data first, then conceptual analysis—the reader may be better prepared not only to see what process led to the conclusions, but also to cope with the partial nature of the approach.

[1] Selznick, Philip, "A Theory of Organizational Commitment" in *Reader in Bureaucracy*, edited by Robert K. Merton and others. The Free Press, Glencoe, Ill., 1952, p. 196.

Finally, mention must be made of the exceedingly controversial nature of the setting. For one thing, medicine itself is surrounded with an incredible amount of emotion. It is all too often discussed by both physicians and laymen, and for that matter by social scientists in a spirit of positively mystical sentimentality. His spokesmen praise the physician for his superhuman qualities; his detractors damn him because he is not superhuman. The patient is defended as one of the poor, timid, Little People, oppressed by wicked, overbearing doctors; he is damned as an ignorant and willfully destructive meddler in medical affairs. Because of the ambivalent emotions that these all-too-common opposites express, I feel it necessary to state that my assumption is that both doctors and patients are human beings, with no more or less vice and virtue than the class implies. I assume that both do the best they can with the abilities they have and that, consonant with my deliberately limited analytical viewpoint, both are no more or less admirable than the structure of circumstances surrounding them allows them to be.

More concretely, I must also observe that the Health Insurance Plan of Greater New York has been the focus of bitter and extended distaste among some segments of organized medicine. It must be said in warning to partisans of both sides that most of the data presented here consist of patients' reports. Obviously, the perspective of the patient is as limited and biased as that of the doctor; each is best taken as only one perspective rather than as the whole truth. If one wishes to accept the accuracy of the patient's perspective when he complains about the Health Insurance Plan medical group, he is also obliged to accept patient complaints about more conventional "private" practitioners. It would be irresponsible and dishonest to do otherwise.

### The Order of Presentation

The major intent of this book is to contribute to the store of ideas about the relation between social structure and professional practice by close examination of some patients and their relation to several modes of organizing medical care. To avoid excessive distortion of the reality involved, the data are to a degree separated from the full-fledged analysis.

In Part One will be presented a description of the medical care programs studied, followed by a fairly extensive examination of what the patients said they wanted from medical programs and how they felt particular programs met their desires. These data on the general expectations of the patients set the stage for the more detailed and problem-oriented data of Part Two. There, attention will be focused on patient behavior that contradicted professional expectations. First, a situation will be analyzed in which patients did not choose and resisted referrals to one type of professional worker within a single medical program. Second, situations will be analyzed in which patients chose not to use the medical care program in which they were enrolled, preferring to use medical services that were organized in a different way. In both situations structural considerations will be emphasized. In Part Three these structural considerations will be examined and elaborated in a more pointed and abstract manner, the intent being to present in the most general and comparative fashion the ideas that emerged from my study.

# PART ONE

## PATIENTS' EVALUATIONS OF THREE MEDICAL PRACTICES

# 1. Three Types of Medical Practice in The Bronx

IN AMERICA there is not just one system of medical care, but many, and these present alternatives among which prospective patients may frequently have occasion to choose. In rural areas there may be choice among folk healers, chiropractors, and physicians.[1] In urban areas there tend to be more alternatives— a large number of physicians to choose from and at least some different kinds of organized practice—clinic, hospital outpatient, and neighborhood practices, for example. Insofar as prospective patients have already had experience with more than one physician or more than one kind of practice, we may assume that their past experience with those alternatives conditions their present choices. In order to begin to understand patient behavior, then, it is necessary to describe the alternatives which confront evaluation and choice, and which have formed the ground of the patients' experience.

## The Health Insurance Plan of Greater New York

Two of the medical practices with which we are concerned operate within the economic and contractual framework of a type of insurance plan that is not very common except in the large cities of the East and West Coasts. This type of plan combines the insurance principle of prepayment with the practice of medicine in organized, multi-physician associations called medical groups. Unlike the most common medical insurance plans, it requires physicians to agree to provide medical services during

[1] See Kibbe, Edward, and Thomas McCorkle, "Culture and Medical Behavior in a Bohemian Speech Community in Iowa," *Bulletin*, no. 1, 1958, Institute of Agricultural Medicine, State University of Iowa.

25

the course of a year in return for a flat annual sum rather than for a fee for each service. In addition, again unlike the most common plans, there is some attempt to see that the physicians involved are qualified to perform the services they provide, and that they perform them competently and conscientiously.

The Health Insurance Plan of Greater New York,[1] formed in 1947, is designed to provide nearly comprehensive coverage of the cost of medical services. The subscriber, with or without the aid of his employer, pays an annual premium, in return for which he (and, depending on the contract, his wife and children) may receive almost all of the medical services he needs in the course of the year for no additional charge. Excluded from coverage are such health items as dental care, drugs and biologicals, spectacles, purely cosmetic surgery, in-hospital anesthesiological services, and treatment for alcoholism, drug addiction, and mental illness. A charge may (but need not) be made for a house-call if it is provided between 10 p.m. and 7 a.m. From a purely economic point of view, a recent study has found[2] the Health Insurance Plan to provide medical services at a comparatively low cost.

The subscriber contracts with the Health Insurance Plan (hereafter to be designated as HIP) for his medical care, but since an insuring organization cannot provide medical care itself, a number of medical groups in Greater New York contract with HIP to provide care. HIP pays the medical groups a set annual fee per subscriber, in return for which the medical groups agree to provide all the services designated in or not excluded from the subscriber's contract. Naturally, the subscriber can obtain those services without extra charge only if he seeks them from the contracting medical group, one of which he must select upon joining the insurance plan.

The medical groups holding contracts with HIP must theoretically conform to a number of requirements.[3] First, there is the

[1] For a recent description and bibliography, see Daily, Edwin F., "Medical Care Under the Health Insurance Plan of Greater New York," *Journal of the American Medical Association*, vol. 170, May 16, 1959, pp. 272–276.

[2] Anderson, Odin W., and Paul B. Sheatsley, *Comprehensive Medical Insurance.* Health Information Foundation Research Series, no. 9, New York, 1959, pp. 24–34.

[3] In the following discussion the author relies heavily upon Health Insurance Plan of Greater New York, *Professional Standards for Medical Groups and Standards for Medical Group Centers Adopted by the Medical Control Board,* 1959.

matter of personnel. Every group must have at least five family physicians and one pediatrician, as well as one board-certified physician in each of the following specialties: dermatology, general surgery, internal medicine, neuropsychiatry, obstetrics and gynecology, ophthalmology, orthopedics, otolaryngology, pathology, radiology, and urology. The qualifications of all physicians affiliated with the medical group must be reviewed and approved by the Medical Control Board of HIP before their appointment, and must conform to such basic standards as meet the requirements of the national medical boards that examine and certify specialists.

Almost all the HIP medical groups are organized as legal partnerships, though part-time participants are not at all uncommon. New physicians usually enter on a salaried basis and after a two-year period, if they and the established partners desire, they assume partnership status. Within five years new partners are supposed to have obtained full voting power in group affairs. Both the partners and those on salary are paid out of the monies remaining in the group from HIP payments after expenses and reserves are provided.

The HIP medical groups are generally organized around a medical center which is located as centrally as possible in its area. Practice varies considerably, but on the whole the specialist services are provided at the medical center and the general medical and pediatric services are provided from the participating physicians' individual offices. Most of the laboratory and other technical facilities are, of course, to be found in the medical center.

Within this operating framework the subscriber is theoretically entitled to an unlimited number of office, home, and hospital services. From the medical group he is entitled to an annual health examination and "necessary" professional services at any time of day or night. (Exactly when a midnight house-call is "really" necessary, however, is a bone of much contention between doctor and patient.) The patient is theoretically free both to choose the medical group by which he wishes to be served (when more than one group covers his area) and, once in the group, to choose any one of the group family physicians to act as his personal physician. For most specialist services he must obtain a referral from his family physician. If he is dissatisfied with his Family Doctor, he may change to another within the same group, or may transfer to another medical group serving the area. He may also complain directly to HIP about his service and expect some investigation of his complaint.

## The Montefiore Hospital Medical Group

As has been noted already, most HIP medical groups are legal partnerships, and many have physicians who treat HIP patients side-by-side with fee-for-service patients in their own individual offices.[1] The Montefiore Hospital Medical Group in the Upper Bronx is the single exception to this rule.[2] It is not a partnership, but rather is hospital-owned:[3] all participating physicians are salaried employees of the hospital and members of the hospital staff. In addition, all the office practice for all Group patients is carried on in the medical center—none of the participating physicians routinely treats subscribers outside the medical center.

Fifty-one physicians participate in providing Group medical services, 13 of the 17 Family Doctors, and 4 of the 6 pediatricians working on a full-time basis; all of the specialists are part-time. Many of the physicians thus divide their time and practice between the Medical Group and their personal non-HIP establishments. There is some annual turnover of Family Doctors; it is not uncommon for a young physician to begin part-time and, as his outside practice builds up, to taper off his time in the Group

[1] For an early and revealing discussion of the experience of one HIP medical group, see Rothenberg, Robert E., Karl Pickard, and Joel E. Rothenberg, *Group Medicine and Health Insurance in Action*, Crown Publishers, New York, 1949.

[2] For a description of the Montefiore Medical Group, see Axelrod, Joseph, "Administrative Aspects of Prepaid Medical Group Practice," unpublished M. S. thesis, School of Public Health, Yale University School of Medicine, 1951; Axelrod, Joseph, "Group Practice of Medicine and Surgery," *Resident Physician*, vol. 2, September, 1956, pp. 37–50; Silver, George A., Martin Cherkasky, and Joseph Axelrod, "An Experience with Group Practice," *New England Journal of Medicine*, vol. 256, April 25, 1957, pp. 785–791.

[3] For a description of Montefiore Hospital's community program, see Silver, George A., "Social Medicine at the Montefiore Hospital: A Practical Approach to Community Health Problems," *American Journal of Public Health*, vol. 48, June, 1958, pp. 724–731.

until he eliminates work at the Center altogether.[1] Turnover is likely to be smaller in groups organized as partnerships.

From the point of view of the patient we may characterize the Montefiore Hospital Medical Group as a centralized and bureaucratized practice in which any amount of virtually any type of medical service may be obtained at no cost beyond the annual premium. Economically, the system is permissive, but medically it is formal: the patient may seek as many Family Doctor[2] or pediatric services as he wishes, but cannot obtain the services of a specialist unless his Family Doctor or pediatrician refers him. Continuity of care is provided by the individual practitioner who is his pediatrician or Family Doctor.

## The Family Health Maintenance Demonstration

The Montefiore Medical Group was the basic framework for the second mode of organizing medical care—the Family Health Maintenance Demonstration.[3] A random sample of families enrolled in the Montefiore Medical Group, the husbands in which were no older than forty-five, was drawn in pairs from the subscriber lists, and a coin toss determined which families would be involved in the Demonstration and which would remain ordinary Montefiore Medical Group patients as "controls." Of the 197 eligible families thus selected as study (rather than control) families, 144 could be communicated with and induced to enter the special program of the Family Health Maintenance Demonstration. Tabulation by a series of economic variables did not reveal any distinctions between the study and control families. And the religious, ethnic, occupational, and educational characteristics of the study families did not differ significantly from those of the Montefiore Medical Group subscribers as a whole.

[1] See Axelrod, Joseph, "Administrative Aspects of Prepaid Medical Group Practice," *op. cit.*, pp. 70–72.

[2] The title "Family Doctors" is used by the Montefiore Medical Group to designate the physicians who supply adults the everyday care that is identified with the general practitioner. At the Montefiore Medical Group all Family Doctors have specialized training in internal medicine.

[3] See Cherkasky, Martin, "Family Health Maintenance Demonstration," *Research in Public Health* (Proceedings of the 1951 Annual Conference of the Milbank Memorial Fund), Milbank Memorial Fund, New York, 1952, pp. 183–194; and the proceedings of a Round Table at the 1953 Annual Conference of the Milbank Memorial Fund entitled, *The Family Health Maintenance Demonstration*, 1954.

As a body, the only important difference that might possibly exist between those subscribers who joined the Demonstration and those who remained regular subscribers in the Montefiore Medical Group was, in the former, a more active, perhaps more anxious attitude toward the Montefiore Medical Group and HIP. Another possible bias existed in the economically advantageous "extra" offered by the Demonstration to those approached—free dental care to the children. No evidence was discovered which might reflect the workings of these possible biases, however, so it is assumed that the Family Health Maintenance Demonstration patients can be treated as representative of the Montefiore Medical Group patients in general.

These patients were invited to participate in a special program of care in which everyday health services were to be provided not by an individual Family Doctor, as is the practice of the Montefiore Medical Group, but by a team composed of a physician, a public health nurse, and a social worker. Instead of using the existent Montefiore Medical Group pediatric and Family Doctor services, with their fairly large panels, a pediatrician and internist were employed to provide care solely to the few Family Health Maintenance Demonstration patients. The relatively small caseload of the physicians involved in everyday care itself allowed them to spend more time with their Demonstration patients than would be the case in ordinary Medical Group practice. In addition, Family Health Maintenance Demonstration practice was not performed solely by physicians. It was organized on a team basis:[1] patients were not only offered the everyday services of Family Doctor and pediatrician, but in addition were encouraged to use the everyday services of a social worker and a public health nurse. Two teams, composed of a social worker and a nurse, divided the participating families between them; the internist and pediatrician participated in both teams. Virtually continuous consultation about the patients took place among team members.

[1] See Silver, George A., and Charlotte Stiber, "The Social Worker and the Physician, Daily Practice of a Health Team," *Journal of Medical Education*, vol. 32, May, 1957, pp. 324–329; Silver, George A., "Beyond General Practice: The Health Team," *Yale Journal of Biology and Medicine*, vol. 31, September, 1958, pp. 29–39.

Introduction and utilization of these professional services was apparently facilitated by the research side of the program. The Demonstration was set up for a number of purposes, not the least of which was the attempt to assess after a five-year period differences in health between the study families and the control families.[1] The research side of the program necessitated systematic gathering and recording of information and professional evaluation of the patients' health, which kept the staff busier than rendering everyday services to 144 families would have done. It also served to introduce the patients to the potential value of the more unfamiliar staff services. The public health nurse, for example, is fairly uncommon in relatively prosperous areas of the city. She was introduced to the patients as a potential resource by pamphlets, referrals, and formal introductions. She also called on the patient in order to evaluate such things as his housing, diet, and recreation.

Indeed, both the research and the preventive sides of the program led to staff behavior that might be described as positive if not aggressive. It was this as much as the team staffing and the low caseload that distinguished the Family Health Maintenance Demonstration from the Montefiore Medical Group and solo practice, for in the former the patient was much more strongly encouraged to use available services liberally. As a result of repeated phone calls he was almost forced to report for an examination. His slightest complaint often received exhaustive attention. Pressures toward utilization in the Family Health Maintenance Demonstration, then, were considerably greater than they were in the Montefiore Medical Group or were likely to be in solo practice.

## Solo Practice

In discussing non-HIP practice, a number of semantic and stylistic barriers confront us. What terms shall we use? Conventionally, non-HIP practice is called "private," but as sensitive spokesmen for HIP are quick to point out, the practice of HIP

[1] For the findings of this study, see the forthcoming report, Silver, George A., *The Family Health Team.*

medical groups can hardly be called "public" in contrast, since the patients do pay for their services and the medical groups receive no public funds to aid in providing services. Thus, HIP offers one form of "private" practice, while the neighborhood doctor offers another. It is possible to talk about HIP and non-HIP practice, but this is neither precise nor graceful. The problem of terminology must here be arbitrarily solved by the alternative use of a number of terms—"solo," "fee-for-service," "neighborhood," "entrepreneurial"—all of which refer to salient differences between HIP and non-HIP practice. In employing these terms, the intention is to refer largely to those practitioners who are used in the everyday course of events—the general practitioner, the pediatrician, and sometimes the internist, the obstetrician-gynecologist, and the ophthalmologist. These are the physicians who are more likely to have neighborhood than downtown or institutional consulting-rooms, and who are thus most likely to represent "private" practice in the patient's eyes. In discussing solo practice, however, one is immediately held in check by the paucity of information available. Though there is a great deal of published opinion, impression, and recollection, there have been very few self-conscious and systematic studies made.[1] Nevertheless, several things can be said that appear to be true and important.

As in many other metropolitan areas, there seem to be enough physicians available in New York City to make solo practice relatively competitive. Fees range from three to five dollars for an office visit to a general practitioner in the Upper Bronx, and five to ten dollars for a home-call. While there is a good deal of complaining by patients about the availability of solo practitioners for home-calls, at least some physicians in Westchester and The Bronx feel it important to their practice to have their night home-calls covered through their answering services by young physicians seeking supplement to their income. The study to be

[1] A notable study is that of Oswald Hall. See his articles: "The Informal Organization of the Medical Profession," *Canadian Journal of Economics and Political Science*, vol. 12, February, 1946, pp. 30–41; "The Stages of the Medical Career," *American Journal of Sociology*, vol. 53, March, 1948, pp. 327–336; "Types of Medical Careers," *American Journal of Sociology*, vol. 55, November, 1949, pp. 243–253.

reported here found a number of cases of Montefiore Medical Group subscribers who used the Medical Group for their daily services, but who also consulted a neighborhood physician willing to render convenient emergency and night service without demanding the right to give daytime care.

As in Chicago,[1] neighborhood practice in The Bronx seems to have a fairly homogeneous group of patients. Italian-American doctors tend to have Italian-American patients; Irish-American doctors tend to have Irish-American patients; Jewish doctors tend to have Jewish patients, but because of the disproportionate number of the former they sometimes "specialize" in patients of ethnic groups other than their own. The relative homogeneity of the solo practitioner's patients is partly a function of the rather limited spatial character of his practice in densely populated, heavily trafficked areas. He seems to recruit most of his patients from a rather small surrounding area which is itself, if not a homogeneous neighborhood, one that contains within it a number of homogeneous and close-knit social networks. More than one network is necessary to sustain a profitable practice, but apparently most patient networks of a single practice are of a similar ethnic and class background. This is of some significance to the way in which solo practice is related to the patient's social life.

## Contrasting Bases of Practice

For our purposes there are some additional characteristics of each type of practice that are very important for evaluating patient responses. One characteristic bears upon what we might reasonably infer to be the quality of medical care and at the same time seems to bear upon the patient's response to the care he gets.

Only a license to practice is required of the solo practitioner. He may choose to limit his practice to pediatrics or gynecology or whatever on the basis of no more than a license. If he does not

[1] See Solomon, David N., "Career Contingencies of Chicago Physicians," unpublished Ph.D. dissertation, University of Chicago, 1952; and Lieberson, Stanley, "Ethnic Groups and the Practice of Medicine," *American Sociological Review*, vol. 23, October, 1958, pp. 542–549.

need the facilities of an accredited hospital, he is free to do whatever falls under that vague rubric "medicine." Furthermore, he may choose to work in complete isolation from his colleagues, entirely escaping their observation. And finally, he may refer his patients for special services to any colleague he sees fit, on the basis of his own judgment. Within very broad limits, he is answerable to nothing but his own judgment and that of his patients, to no person but himself and his patients. If patient demand exceeds doctor supply, he may not even be answerable to his patients. It follows from this that the quality of care is likely to fluctuate widely from one solo practice to another, varying with the individual characteristics of the practitioner, the security of his practice, and the sophistication and pressure of his patients' judgment.

In contrast, both the Montefiore Medical Group and the Family Health Maintenance Demonstration function in a bureaucratic context that engenders a fair degree of standardization and calculability in the behavior of professional workers. The Medical Control Board of HIP lays down minimum standards for all participating physicians, so that each one in a particular specialty, whether pediatrics or thoracic surgery, has much the same professional preparation as any other in the same specialty. Furthermore, unlike solo practice, practice both in the Montefiore Medical Group and in the Family Health Maintenance Demonstration is subject to observation, indeed inspection, by colleagues both within and outside the organizations. Referrals may only be to similarly qualified and observable colleagues. It follows from this that the quality of care is more likely to be fairly standardized, as is the professional behavior of the practitioners, and is less likely to depend upon, or be highly responsive to, the evaluations of patients.

The contrast is intensified when we examine the manner in which patients are recruited. First, in the Montefiore Medical Group the patients are not recruited by each other as they are in solo practice. They are recruited by the impersonal mechanism of a contract signed in a workplace. There is some coercion of the city workers, for while they can choose to join HIP or not, if they choose not to join, the city will not pay a portion of the premiums for the quite separate hospitalization insurance ("Blue Cross"). Thus, in the Montefiore Medical Group there is essentially no contract between the patient and an individual physician: the contract is between the patient and an insurance plan that guarantees to provide a qualified physician.

There may be positive attraction or repulsion exerted by the principle of a prepaid group practice plan, by the reputation of a medical group in the area of residence, by the gossip of work associates, or by friends who have heard about or experienced the plan, but in contrast to solo practice, recruitment of patients in the Montefiore Medical Group is essentially impersonal. The Montefiore Medical Group itself is fairly large, serving about 23,000 adults (plus 4,000 children) in an area inhabited by at least 200,000 adults. While the selection of subscribers from the area is hardly random, involving as it does enrollment of some union locals which have cooperative housing projects, and city departments (some employees of whom become concentrated in city housing projects), subscribers to the Medical Group are a minority, residing in a densely populated area where everyone does not know everyone else. There is every likelihood that patients are recruited without reference to the recommendations of friends, relatives, and neighbors. If subscribers should ask their friends and neighbors to recommend a good doctor, the chances are that it will *not* be a Montefiore Medical Group doctor who is recommended, not because the doctor is not "good" but because their associates are more likely to "know" solo practitioners. The Medical Group, then, is likely to stand outside the everyday method laymen use to select doctors.[1]

All of this makes it likely that Montefiore Medical Group subscribers will be strangers to one another, not common members of lay referral systems which are connected with the Group. This is directly opposite to the case of the patients of a neighborhood

[1] In a national survey more than 50 per cent of those with a "regular doctor" reported that they first used him because of recommendations of relatives, friends, neighbors, or co-workers. This National Opinion Research Center survey, financed by the Health Information Foundation, will soon be reported by Jacob J. Feldman and Paul B. Sheatsley. It will be referred to here as the NORC-HIF survey.

practitioner. In this sense, the Montefiore Medical Group patient is likely to respond to his Group family doctors more helplessly than as a member of a network of fellow-patients. He will have no source of support for belief in the virtues of his Group physicians beyond his own experience and the formal designation of professional qualifications which the Medical Group may make available to him on request. The physician in the Medical Group is thus more likely than the physician in neighborhood practice to have no lay reputation of significance, practicing medicine solely on the basis of his professional reputation. The physicians are vouched for by the professional standards of the Medical Group and the Medical Control Board of HIP, not by fellow-patients.

In one sense the Family Health Maintenance Demonstration is significant because it may stand somewhere in between the two types of practice we have already discussed. It does indeed share the impersonal contractual arrangement, the medical center and the "quality controls" of its parent, the Montefiore Medical Group. Patients, however, were *invited* into the Demonstration, which was a special program. It is possible that they felt themselves to be a special, privileged group—a feeling unlikely to exist either among ordinary patients of solo practitioners or of the Montefiore Medical Group. Certainly a sense of being set apart was likely to have been encouraged by the attentions lavished upon them by the Demonstration staff and the easy availability of a variety of professional workers, some of whom were separated from the patient by less social distance than is the case for physicians. These considerations, as well as the simple fact that the Demonstration program involved a much broader range of health services, make of it a special, third type of practice.

### Patients in the Upper Bronx

The area of New York City in which the three practices are found is one that finds kinship with areas in other large American cities which have had intimate association with the waves of European immigration that marked the earlier part of this century.[1] The area is a product of the sifting and sorting process

[1] Besides interviews and Medical Group records, the author's two-year residence in the Upper Bronx is the basis for the following sketch.

of past ecological mobility on the part of immigrants, fairly stable now even in the face of the distant push of an expanding Puerto Rican and Negro population in the Lower Bronx.

Forty years ago the area immediately around Montefiore Hospital was almost open countryside, with few residents. At that time it was a place to which modestly successful immigrants moved, building their detached one and two-family houses as both an investment and a place in the country in which to rear their children. Small pockets of those homes—two or three adjacent tree-lined streets—still exist throughout the area as a testament to the quasi-suburban character of that early movement.

But in many streets in The Bronx we find a few of those houses crammed between high apartment buildings. Another kind of movement formed the present character of The Bronx—the movement from Manhattan of immigrants who obtained steady and respectable jobs but not the success necessary for investment in land and a home. Attracted to the Upper Bronx both by increasingly extensive public transportation and a prospect of more "trees and fresh air" for the children, they began filling the new apartment buildings in increasing numbers, as well as, to the East, drab rows of detached and semi-detached two-family homes apparently built for speculative purposes.

Whatever bloom had been on The Bronx from its property owners was more or less rubbed off by this influx of apartment dwellers, in spite of some attempt to sustain the Grand Concourse as a "prestige" address. The area is now rather thoroughly permeated with the ethos and style of what is suggested by Vidich and Bensman's term, "the marginal middle class,"[1] qualified by Jewish, Italian, and Irish ethnic subcultures. And it is now a settled place where it is not at all unusual to find people who have been brought up, have married, and have begun to bring up children all within an area of a few blocks.

[1] In spite of the rural locale of their study, Vidich and Bensman's characterization of the marginal middle class makes sense for The Bronx. See Vidich, Arthur J. and Joseph Bensman, *Small Town in Mass Society*, Anchor Books, New York, 1960, pp. 62–66. Also relevant here is Mills, C. Wright, *White Collar*, Oxford University Press, New York, 1951, as are the characterizations of "The Common Man Level" by W. Lloyd Warner and his associates, and of "Class III" and "Class IV" by August B. Hollingshead.

Its stability is manifested in marked and very public patterns of sociability—indeed, it almost outdoes the stereotype of the small town if only because people are too crowded in their apartments to stay behind the privacy of their apartment doors. The elderly very often bring out aluminum chairs and sit on the sidewalks, scrutinize passersby, and listen to and argue with their daughters. Many wives shop daily, making their rounds of the grocery store, the meat market, the dairy and egg market, the fish market, the fruit and vegetable market, and, less regularly, the notions store, the shoemaker, the dry cleaner, and the specialty clothing or hosiery store. In good weather at the peak of the day in the shopping areas, the pedestrian must often walk in the street in order to get by the great knots of women talking behind their baby carriages and wheeled market baskets on the sidewalk. It is within these clusters that the women talk about the illness in their families, compare symptoms, remedies, the names and characteristics of the doctors they have seen, the treatments they have obtained at what suffering, and the outcome of their search for cures.

It must not be thought that the Upper Bronx is an intimate social group, or even that localities or neighborhoods within it are such. Everybody does not know and interact with everybody else. Some physical neighbors may not be social neighbors. Outside the nuclear family, life in The Bronx, like that in London, goes on through the medium of fairly stable and homogeneous networks of friends and relatives, not through closed and well-organized social groups.[1] These networks are influenced by space so they are likely to be more often local than not, but given the telephone and the automobile they are not entirely restricted to a narrow local area. It is by reference to these homogeneous networks of gossip that we are able to understand how individuals living in a heterogeneous environment may nonetheless have largely consistent and homogeneous experience.

That in its composition the Upper Bronx is hardly homogeneous, we may see from examination of the attributes of the

[1] For a more detailed discussion of such networks in London, see Bott, Elizabeth, "Urban Families: Conjugal Roles and Social Networks," *Human Relations*, vol. 8, 1955, pp. 345-384.

patients of the Montefiore Hospital Medical Group. The patients of the Medical Group are all residents of the urban and faintly suburban area of the Upper Bronx and Lower West-chester Counties, on the northern outskirts of the City of New York. About 75 per cent of the patients live within an area of ten heavily trafficked square miles of apartments and multi-family dwellings. They are largely divided between being city employees and being skilled and semi-skilled workers whose unions have negotiated fringe benefits involving a contract with HIP for medical care. It is from the city employee group that the greatest heterogeneity stems, for in this category are found professors of the city college system, United Nations personnel, engineers, nurses in city hospitals, schoolteachers, social workers, clerks, policemen, firemen, subway sweepers, sanitation truck drivers, and many more—occupationally, a wide range from the high prestige professional to the semi-skilled worker. Variety is also reflected in the wide range of educational backgrounds found in a 1957 sample of subscribers: 21 per cent had no more than an elementary school education; 38 per cent went no further than high school; 27 per cent had at least some college training but held no degree higher than the B.A.; 14 per cent had college postgraduate training. Heterogeneity in education and occupation is matched by heterogeneity in religious and ethnic background—27 per cent are foreign-born; 51 per cent are Jewish, 36 per cent are Catholic, and 11 per cent Protestant; 17 per cent are of Italian parentage and 19 per cent of Irish ancestry. Two per cent reported no religious affiliation.

The proportion of subscribers with a higher education is not representative of the Upper Bronx as a whole, for the city employees who are professors and schoolteachers have biased the distribution. Typically, as has been noted already, the resident of the Upper Bronx is a member of the marginal middle class, most often with only a high school education. His culture involves a very strong emphasis on the traditional middle class virtues of independence and thrift: typically, economic aspirations are either to own a small shop (run by all members of the family during all hours of the day and night and doomed to early bankruptcy) or to own a home in Queens or Long Island. These aspirations are pursued by rigid though not very systematic restriction of consumption—most often, apparently, by spending as little as possible on housing and getting along in the smallest number of rooms, and the steady addition of small sums of money to a savings bank account. Further, the culture of The Bronx involves the traditional middle class virtue of cleanliness— what seems to professional workers an inordinate and compulsive preoccupation with being and staying clean, with keeping the household (though not the neighborhood) orderly and free of superficial dust. In health affairs the culture of The Bronx is expressed by behavior that impresses professional workers as hysterical—agitated fright in the face even of minor illness, particularly if children are involved. Response to illness is complicated by the fact that the citizen of The Bronx seems often not at all sure that the outsiders connected with education, medical care, sanitation—indeed, any service that "they" are responsible for—are entirely devoted to his rather than someone else's welfare. He therefore tends to be suspicious of those outsiders, jealous of what he sees to be his rights, and fearful of being "pushed around" or "taken advantage of." The net result is a tendency to be latently hostile, quick to complain, or even take legal action when he feels he has been mistreated.

# 2. Patient Attitudes Toward Medical Care

Now that we know something of the patients and the practices with which they have been confronted, we may ask what it is the patients ask of medical care, and what criteria they use in deciding whether what they want is present or not. Their demands are, of course, made in the light of their past experience and the expectations that stem from it. And while these patients are "dissatisfied" enough with their present experience to have some unrealized ideal in mind, they nonetheless may be taken to manifest a practical satisfaction with the present.

This practical satisfaction should be kept in mind when trying to assess responses toward medical care, for it underlies both the routine passivity of the patient who accepts without much question what is given to him, and the "ingratitude" he shows for something he has had when he is offered something else. The patient's tendency to accept practical compromises with the ideal is best seen in individual case histories, where responses to changing events may be observed over time. Two case histories will illustrate the point and serve to introduce analysis of patient attitudes.

Both of the families in these case histories were in the "control group" of the Family Health Maintenance Demonstration; they had not been given care by the Demonstration, having experienced only the entrepreneurial care available to them before joining HIP and the care available within HIP to regular subscribers of the Montefiore Medical Group. The material presented is from the interviewer's report, which was dictated immediately after the interview. There has been some editing of the material for the sake of clarity, and some for the sake of protecting the identity both of the patients and of their physicians. Names are, of course, fictitious, and some symptoms have been changed to aid in protecting identity. The informants' statements are not necessarily true, for they represent *responses* to facts rather than facts as such.

### Two Case Histories

An interview with a semi-skilled city worker and his wife, both of Irish descent and with a high school education, is reported below.

> The couple were asked for a chronology of their experience with medical services. The husband's family had a family doctor whom he had seen once or twice when he was younger, but he reported he couldn't remember him. He and his wife had no regular physician before their children arrived. The doctor who delivered their first child was drafted soon afterward. They had no physician again until the second pregnancy. During this pregnancy the wife had the services of an obstetrician who agreed to take care of her and the baby only for six weeks following delivery. However, she heard from someone that there was a wonderful pediatrician in the neighborhood—her dentist's doctor. She asked the local druggist about the doctor; the druggist recommended him very highly. So she began going to this "pediatrician." He delivered her third baby and took care of the whole family for a number of years, right up to the time they went into HIP.
>
> The wife was asked whether she liked the doctor and she said he was just wonderful. She said, "He was always so calm and quiet. He was always a good influence on me—calming me down. He'd come over and say, 'Well, now, don't get excited, let's look at this thing. It really doesn't seem to be so bad. The thing we should do is take it easy and not worry about it.' " She liked this physician more than any other she had, because, she said, "I think probably the biggest thing is you have the feeling he takes really a very strong personal interest in you." And here the husband said, "Yes, you know what he does on his vacation? He goes to Holy Name Hospital to study up on his pediatrics and cardiology." The implication I felt the husband intended to convey here was that the doctor had a measure of dedication to his craft that other doctors lack.

In exploring the wife's responses to this doctor I got several examples of what she felt to be interest in the family. Once all three children came down with dysentery at the same time and she telephoned the doctor. When he looked at them, she reported him to say, " 'Well, if I took them into the hospital I could get rid of this in twenty-four hours, but hospitals have been known to upset kids, so maybe it'd be better to take a little longer time to cure them and keep them home.' " So he showed her how to feed them glucose through the rectum and told her to keep in constant touch with him on the phone. Actually, she reported, within twenty-four hours the thing cleared up anyway. . . . On all occasions, the wife said, the doctor never seemed rushed, though her husband added at this point that he seemed to have an enormous practice. The wife said he was always slow and easy-going and always explained things to her. In the course of the discussion the husband added, "Well, he's like the old-time family doctor." [Do not forget that this man recalls nothing about his boyhood family doctor.] I asked him what he meant and he said, "Well, you know, anyone, me or my wife, can sort of drop in and talk to him about one thing or another and you can talk to him about anything. It doesn't make any difference, he's very helpful no matter what it is."

When HIP was organized, however, the husband decided he'd join it if only as a matter of insurance, and when he told the doctor about it, the doctor said, "Fine," and let it go at that. The husband interpreted the doctor's response as approval of HIP for patients whose income is below a certain level.

But when this couple first joined HIP, the wife was very much upset, for she had to select a pediatrician from a panel and she didn't know whom to select. The one she finally picked she disliked very much. I asked her why and she said, "Well, she was very sharp and curt, and she frightened the children. Like, the children came in the first time and what she did was point to the table and say to them, 'Get on the table,' and they burst out crying because they were used to our private doctor who always acted in a different way." After that examination the wife asked to have another pediatrician and she's been fairly satisfied. When the children became older and no longer needed pediatric services, they all went to the mother's Montefiore Medical Group Family Doctor.

As to the Family Doctors (rather than pediatricians) she experienced in the Montefiore Medical Group, the wife liked her first one, but he left the Group shortly after she met him. She disliked the second one intensely and never went back to him after the first examination.

When he left the Group she selected a third Family Doctor, the one whom she had at the time of the interview. At this point the husband said that he didn't like the turnover of doctors in the Medical Group. He said, "One thing about a family doctor, he should know you and you should know him, so if anything comes up he knows you thoroughly." He added that familiarity also obviates the nuisance of repeating a detailed history.

I asked the wife why she didn't like the second Family Doctor she had had at the Medical Group and she told me about her kidney condition. When she was about nineteen years old she first began to have pain in her kidneys. She went to an entrepreneurial physician about the pain, and he apparently suggested that she wait to see what happened. She let it go. After she joined HIP, however, her kidneys began to hurt a great deal and she went in to see her Family Doctor. He had x-rays and other tests taken and she described her consultation with him as follows: "He came in and said, 'Hello,' and looked at the slips from the tests and said, 'You have kidney stones.' Then he said, 'You have to have them out, there's nothing else that can be done.' " She wanted to ask him questions about how necessary an operation really was, whether the stones could be passed, and the like, but he simply cut her off and said, " 'You just have to have them out, there's nothing else that can be done.' " She wanted to think things over, hesitating to rush into the operation, but the doctor irritated her so by not answering her questions that she never went back to him.

Finally, he left the Group. The kidney condition became worse, so she went in and chose a new Family Doctor. She reported him as saying after he examined her, " 'Well, you certainly have large kidney stones. The best thing for you to do would be to have them out, or else they're going to be a constant source of pain, which will probably increase as the years go by. You just think it over and then come back and talk to me about it. We'll see what we can do. But I want to say again that an operation is the only thing that is likely to stop this pain and that will prevent severe difficulties in the future.' " She underwent surgery soon thereafter, has felt well since, and is very pleased with her Montefiore Medical Group Family Doctor. If money were no object, though, she had little doubt that she would return to the neighborhood physician she had before joining HIP.

In spite of this ultimate preference for the neighborhood physician, both insisted they liked HIP very much. There was really very little they would say against it, and only by a little teasing were they induced to talk about some of the things they felt were shortcomings. The husband said, "Oh, of course, I know a lot of people tell me it's no good; they have to wait too long, they can never get a doctor for a house-call, and so forth, but I still think it's pretty good." I asked him whether he had had any particular trouble getting a doctor and he said, "Well, we're not the kind of people who phone the doctor the first minute—we wait and see how things are going to come out. And we realize how hard it is for the doctor to get to our home, so we don't bring up the problem. But I know there's lots of people who start screaming for their doctors as soon as the kid has a belly-ache."

He went on to explain that part of his enthusiasm lay in his wife's successful kidney-stone operation the Christmas before the interview, and the "wonderful" way she was treated. Several years before that, their son was also operated on and they were pleased with the treatment and the results. "So," the husband said, "just on the insurance angle HIP has been a wonderful thing for us. Why, I'd still be in hock for those things I've had there. I couldn't pay it in ten years. . . ."

Upon further questioning he commented that some people he knew have complained about HIP. "Well," he said, "it's sort of like a clinic and they have a feeling that this is a clinic, and they don't really like it." And I said to him, "Well, it is a kind of clinic, isn't it?" The husband said, "Well, yeah, there are those long rows of benches and you have to take your turn and to go through that way, and there's a lot of people waiting. It isn't as if you were in a little private doctor's office where there are just a few people waiting. So I suppose it is sort of a clinic, but then what can you expect when you have a setup like this and they have to take care of so many people?"

In this case history, we begin to get some impression of the span of years and experience that contributes to present attitudes. However, the family had a relatively sanguine attitude toward medical authority as such. It is, in fact, a fairly atypical family, presented because it represents an extreme. The following case history presents the opposite extreme—fear and suspicion. The husband is a semi-skilled city worker and both he and his wife are high school graduates, of Italian descent.

To the general question, "How do you like HIP?" the answer was, "Just wonderful." I asked the husband what he had not liked about

HIP and he said that sometimes he gets the feeling that he's being treated like a charity case, and after all, he's paying his money and he wants to be treated just like anybody else. I asked him what he meant and he said, "Well, for one thing, when I feel I'm sick or somebody else in the family is sick, I want the doctor to come over and see me, not just try to prescribe over the phone and tell me to come in the next morning." He then referred to his experience in another HIP medical group, before he moved into the Montefiore area of service, where he had a much stronger feeling of being a charity case. I asked him what made him feel like a charity case in the other group and he said, "Well, they didn't seem to take you seriously, I mean they didn't seem to want to do anything for you, like if you feel there's something wrong and you want to have an x-ray or something like that, what the doctor in the other group did was just tell you, 'Don't worry about it, you're all right, don't worry about it, you don't need any x-rays.' "

Turning to the wife's history, her first regular doctor was that of her parents. Her parents had consulted him for some time until the mother felt he was getting too old and switched to a younger one. I asked the mother, who was present at the interview, just what it was that led her to change doctors. She was noncommittal and simply said, "He was very nice, and we liked him very much, but we just felt he was getting old and we wanted a younger doctor, that's all." She expressed no sorrow or reluctance at transferring to another.

The second doctor for the wife's family was at first described in a very neutral way—he was all right, he was very nice, and so on. Then the wife said, "Well, you know one thing about Doctor Able is he was too jolly about things. I'd come in feeling bad about something and he'd say, 'Don't worry about it, don't worry about it,' and he'd slap me on the back and he'd laugh. He was very jolly, but I really didn't get treated for anything. He was nice, but I had the feeling he really wasn't doing all he could for me."

At the time this young woman married, her husband was already a member of HIP, so she began using the services of a HIP physician in a medical group other than Montefiore. She didn't like him very much. She said, "He'd be in his shirt-sleeves when I saw him, he didn't wear a white coat, and his office was so dirty. It didn't look like a doctor's office at all—there were things scattered all around. And he didn't take me very seriously. I got real mad at him because he kept saying I should have a baby. I had hay fever for several months one summer and I went to see the doctor three or four times about the hay fever. I guess I was calling him up quite a bit too, because I'd be sneezing, my eyes would be watering, and my nose all swollen up. And he didn't give me any kind of treatment. He'd just say, 'Why don't you have a baby? This may all clear up if you have a baby.' And you know, it's a funny thing, but I had a baby the next year and I never have had trouble with hay fever since."

When the family moved into the Montefiore area they transferred to the Montefiore Group. Shortly afterward the wife became pregnant and was delivered by a HIP obstetrician. She said, "He was a wonderful man. I was frightened, I had great fears, and I didn't know what pregnancy was like, or delivery, or anything like that. He was very nice, I mean he explained everything to me. He told me not to worry, that he'd take care of everything. He told me he'd be there to deliver the baby in time. I had perfect faith in him, and he was there. He was just wonderful. He was so good I referred a girl who lives in the same apartment here to him for her baby, and she just raved about him, too, as a private patient."

She did not, however, like her pediatrician. "She just made fun of everything that worried me," the wife said, "and she seemed kind of short with me. She was a very good doctor, but I really wasn't very happy with her." Difficulty getting house-calls began to be serious. The wife said, "I was already used to having them ask about temperature over the phone, and having to tell them the baby was throwing up but didn't have a temperature. They wouldn't come over; they told me to bring her in, in the morning. But once the doctor told me to bring the baby in, and when I did, she apologized and said the baby should have stayed in bed. Another time the baby had the croup and I had to call the doctor three or four times before she came, about six in the morning. They'd say on the phone, 'Just bathe her, put her in a bath to keep her cool, and give her aspirin.' "

By the time the baby was six months old the wife was so upset about the difficulty she felt the HIP doctors put in the way of making house-calls that she asked a friend of hers to recommend a "private" pediatrician. She took the child to the neighborhood pediatrician for some months until suddenly one night the baby took on a high temperature. She called the pediatrician immediately, but he refused to come out because it was nighttime, telling her to sponge the baby with cool water, give her aspirin, and bring her in to see him in the morning, that there was no point in his coming then because there wasn't much he could do. The wife was very upset by this, for she felt the baby was quite sick and that some doctor should see her. Her husband suggested that she call HIP. She did, and within fifteen minutes a doctor came and said, " 'This baby's very sick,' " and gave her a shot, saying she had roseola. The next morning her regular HIP pediatrician called and said, "You haven't been down to see us for a long time, we haven't seen your child. Why don't you use your HIP services?" So from that time on the wife had not used a neighborhood physician, believing that entrepreneurial services are as bad as HIP, so far as house-calls go. She also confessed that because the HIP doctors were so reluctant to come out on a call, if the baby doesn't have a temperature, she has learned to say she does have one. If it's only 102, she tells the doctor on the phone that it is 104, just to make sure that he will come.

So far as her experience with her own Family Doctor (rather than pediatrician) goes, she isn't entirely satisfied. Sometimes she feels he doesn't take her seriously enough. He keeps telling her not to worry and that there's nothing really wrong with her, and she sometimes feels that he should be a little more sympathetic.

As to the husband, he had had almost no contact with physicians before joining HIP. Recently, however, he had felt his heart skip a beat when he performed the occasionally dangerous task required by his work, and he had an unnatural sensation in his chest; he felt as though there was a bone bearing down on his stomach. It was to ask for an x-ray of this area that he went to the doctor in the first HIP group to which he belonged. The husband was rather irritated by the doctor's attempt to discourage an x-ray, for he felt he had a right to an x-ray if he wanted one. When he changed medical groups, he went to his new Family Doctor and told him about his symptoms and the doctor said, "Well, I think what we might do is, you make an appointment and we'll give you a complete medical checkup just to make sure!" After the checkup, which included x-rays, the doctor said everything checked out perfectly, the patient was in fine shape and had nothing to worry about. That seemed to have quieted his fears.

The attitudes toward medicine expressed in these two cases are quite different: in one there is little preoccupation with illness as such, and a relatively large amount of confidence in medicine and physicians in general; in the other, there is constant preoccupation with bodily functions, and some suspicion of the physician. But it happens that both use the same criteria in evaluating medical care. Indeed, in every intensive interview there were expressed two major criteria: first, in desirable medical care the practitioner must have *interest* in his patient; second, in desirable medical care the physician must be *competent*. These two criteria, advanced spontaneously in a large variety of contexts by all those interviewed, will serve to organize our conception of what patients want from medical care. As a central aspect of patient culture, it must be discussed in some detail before turning to the patients' evaluation of the care they actually obtain.

Prefatory to discussing these criteria we must note that the kind of choice best illuminated by this material is not the sort that is made when one first selects a physician. As will be noted later, the lay referral system, accident, and locality are involved in initial choice rather than personal experience. The choice illuminated by our discussion here is rather that which is involved in deciding to go back to a doctor or to consult another instead, and in making reluctant and rare, or willing and frequent, use of a particular physician. Insofar as this choice is not guided either by lay consultants or by the physician's own referral, it depends on the experience the individual himself has in the consulting-room. It is to that experience and the manner in which it is evaluated by the patient that we may turn now.

### Personal Interest

It is not entirely faithful to the facts to discuss the criteria of interest and competence as two separate entities, for in free interviews where simple statements could be most fully explored the patients were rather insistent that one could not very well exist without the other. The pressure of rhetoric would lead one man to say, "Sometimes I think it's a lot more important to me that I be treated as a person when I go to a doctor than that I get the best medical care." The deliberate pressure of an overly simple set of alternative answers to the question, "If you had to pick one doctor out of a group, what kind would you choose?" could force 80 per cent of those 576 Montefiore Medical Group subscribers who answered to choose doctors demonstrating personal interest alone or competence alone.[1] However, reality seems somewhat less distinct. Keeping this in mind, we may nonetheless separate the two temporarily as the patients themselves do, for the purpose of discussion.

*Interest* is manifested to the patient by a number of characteristics, some of which are more important to one individual than another. Some of the patients seem to appreciate a joking familiarity, as the following comparison[2] made by an upper-lower class male indicates:

> He was a cold fish. He'd say hello and call you by name, but he was a lot different from the doctor we have at HIP. When my wife was expecting, this HIP doctor told us his wife was, too, and he'd joke about the babies being neck and neck, or belly and belly.

Other patients prefer a more reserved manner on the part of the physician, showing concern that he doesn't "go over a certain line" or "take liberties" in his relationship with them. It appears to be the lower-middle and particularly upper-middle class patient who is most likely to prefer reserve, or in any case to profess little need for extraverted expressions of common humanity and sympathy from the physician. An upper-middle class wife's comment on the opposite page illustrates this toleration of reserve.

[1] At about the same time that this conclusion was made, Rose Coser's paper was published in *Social Problems*. Coser found two "basically different images of the doctor" in hospital patients' remarks—one involving competence and the other involving an omnipotent figure dispensing protection and love. She classified patients by their emphasis on the one image or the other, and attempted to show in a very interesting and perceptive way how these emphases are important for variable patient behavior in hospitals. See Coser, Rose Laub, "A Home Away from Home" in *Sociological Studies of Health and Sickness*, edited by Dorian Apple, McGraw-Hill Book Co., New York, 1959, pp. 154–172.

From my interviews I remained unconvinced that a significant number of the patients studied could be classified in this way irrespective of social class; that is, that such an orientation to the doctor was independent of social class. And, indeed, a subsequent questionnaire item designed to allow tabulation of patients by such orientations to doctors proved relatively unprofitable. Other variables, as we shall see, were far more critical in their association with such patient behavior as shopping around and in particular the use of outside services.

The failure to find significance in Coser's distinction, however, may very well have been due to the question I used. For a set of questionnaire items that are worth further exploration, see Hassinger, Edward W., and Robert L. McNamara, "Relationships of the Public to Physicians in a Rural Setting," *Research Bulletin*, no. 653, University of Missouri Agricultural Experiment Station, January, 1958, pp. 20–21.

[2] The reader should note that the patients quoted throughout this chapter are not talking solely about HIP doctors. In the patient's comment quoted at this point, a "private" doctor is being compared with a HIP doctor.

My HIP doctor isn't as personal as our old family doctor, but we do like him because he's such a nice person. He doesn't go in for the bedside manner, but he's an excellent diagnostician and he's very conservative in his treatment. Don't misunderstand me, though, he's *not* impersonal and he does want to do the best for us. [Interviewer: What do you mean by impersonal?] Well, a feeling that he doesn't care, that he works mechanically.

All patients seem to agree that one symptom of interest is the extent to which the doctor is willing to talk to them. In the interviews the words "curt" and "abrupt" recur again and again as epithets describing uninterested physicians. These words sometimes occurred in a context in which the patient apparently had no desire to communicate anything he had not already communicated, and no desire for additional information. In such a context the epithets imply that the physician is not acknowledging them as significant beings, and is working mechanically rather than with interested and sympathetic concern for their difficulties.

In other instances, these words occur in a context that, after probing, indicates behavior which discourages questions the patients want to ask, and if patients did ask questions, not answering them to their satisfaction. Often, as in the following example from an upper-lower class husband, the pressure of time is clearly connoted.

The doctor just seemed to look her over in a very cursory way. He was very curt. This was her first baby and my wife didn't know what to expect. She was kind of frightened and he didn't tell her anything about, you know, what to expect or how to behave. He didn't do anything; I mean he seemed to be trying to rush her out of the office as soon as possible. I had the feeling that he was thinking he had lots more patients waiting and wishing we'd hurry up. . . . He'd just sort of grunt when he examined you and then write out a prescription and not say anything. He really didn't treat you like a personality; he didn't seem to be interested. We felt we were just part of his business, like those ten garages he owned in the neighborhood which he was always renting to someone.

Curtness and abruptness thus involve not only the feeling that the physician is not concerned with the attempt of the patient to understand his illness and the regimen necessary to cure it, or with the emotions which he as a person invests in his difficulty, but also that the physician has allocated only a small period of time to the patient. The allocation might very well be adequate for diagnosing and treating the machinery of the body, but it leaves no room for an encounter with the personal identity which the patient imputes to his own body.

Personal identity is basically at issue for the patient. It is a truism, of course, that in order to do his work effectively the physician must in some sense be able to strip the identity from the patient's body as he works on it so as not to lose his objectivity, but it is that very identity which is the most precious assertion of the patient, and its loss, when it is apparent, seems to be rather unpleasant.[1] It is very easy to be mawkish, and consequently blind to the very real contrary demands of practice itself in discussing this side of the patient role, but the degree to which the patients studied were preoccupied with it was strikingly intense. To them, a satisfactory physician must seem to take enough personal interest in them so that they will feel no threat to their identities as persons.

## Competence in History-Taking and Examination

Personal interest does more than support the patient's sense of identity. It also serves to indicate the quality of attention the physician will pay to his difficulties. It is this that is connoted by the word "automatic." When the body is seen as a machine with standard parts made according to standard specifications, it may be treated merely by rote, without the inquiring and sympathetic intelligence that is necessary to treat what the patients believe to be an entirely different and mysterious order of reality—a person. In their view of themselves as unique "cases," rather than individual manifestations of a standard plan, the patients accept the ideology of the profession itself, which insists that every case

[1] Many writers have commented on the way being unclothed in the consultation room attacks the patient's sense of identity. Potter, however, suggests that if one acts the proper way when unclothed it is the doctor who loses his identity and becomes a personal servant whose intimate knowledge of his master's blemishes and vices is a function of his lack of importance. See Potter, Stephen, *One-Upmanship*, Henry Holt and Co., New York, 1953, p. 32.

requires complex judgments that cannot be obtained from a book of rules. Consequently, lack of personal interest not only makes the patients feel uncomfortable, but also implies to them that the attention they are getting may not be sufficiently well motivated to allow the proper competence to be practiced.

However, it should be understood that the patients assume that all doctors possess a minimal competence. No patient damned the profession as a whole, and for that matter none of the patients who were interviewed expressed the belief that a particular physician was so incompetent that he should not be allowed to practice. In trying to evaluate a doctor's competence, then, patients are concerned with relative rather than absolute differences. They seek to determine who is *most* competent. What criteria do they use?

One of the first events that occur in the consultation room is history-taking and the physical examination. The way in which these are performed seems to play a large part in patients' evaluation of the physician's competence, for the patients make much of the physician who "just looked at me," or who gave a "perfunctory examination," or who did not ask about prior outbreaks of the same symptoms. Patients, of course, vary considerably in the sophistication of their expectations. Some, especially those in the lower class, have only a vague idea of what concrete questions and examinations to expect. What seems important to them is the physician's attentiveness and deliberate care rather than any specific techniques. They tend to use time as a simple behavioral measure, thoroughness becoming synonymous with the consumption of time and the appearance of deliberateness.

Other patients, likely to be better educated, are more specific about their demands. They expect a wide variety of examination techniques and feel dismayed when the physician just "checks your heart, your pressure, looks at your eyes, ears, nose, and throat, pats you around a little and that's the end of it." They tend to have a rather definite, and what they believe to be an informed and rational, conception of what it is that troubles them. Some of them collect observations systematically about their difficulty over a period of time—for example, collecting information on the presence of an allergic reaction when diet or some portion of the physical environment is changed. If the physician should not ask about these things in his history-taking, and should wave away the symptoms they report, they may question in their own minds his competence to diagnose their difficulty "correctly." If, on the other hand, he should ignore attempts to give information about the relation of allergic reaction to environment and diet, and without comment administer patch tests, they may not feel suspicion of his competence so much as be chagrined and resent his deprecation of their ability to give reliable information.[1] Their chagrin seems to be a partial function of status, for the upper-middle class patient tends to believe that he is a near-equal of the physician in education, sophistication, and reliability, and he is well aware of how close his social class is to that of the physician.

Above and beyond what the physician himself does in taking a history and performing with his own hands his examination, all patients seem agreed that the greater the quantity of "objective" tests—for example, blood pressure, x-rays, electrocardiogram—the better the quality of medicine that is being practiced. This criterion is only partly connected with the evaluation of the physician's own competence, however, for it is not entirely free of economic considerations. Where economic considerations are ostensibly not important—as in the Medical Group, or with patients who feel so much anxiety that money is no object for them—the more tests the better. While a physician who has technical resources readily available is not himself considered more competent, their availability is believed to allow him to practice more competently.

### Competence in Diagnosis and Prescription

After the examination there is, of course, the diagnosis and prescribed regimen. Diagnosis and prescription may be rejected out of hand when patients are told that their condition is not serious and that they should stop worrying. In that case, patients

---

[1] Deprecation of the patient's intellectual capacities is another way for the doctor to be "One-up," as Potter has observed; *op. cit.*, p. 34.

have frequently concluded that the physician does not perceive the "real" quality of their complaint, and instead of following his advice they consult another physician. Other patients, particularly those with chronic but relatively minor (and essentially mysterious) complaints like headaches and upper respiratory infection symptoms which are later diagnosed as allergies, do indeed stop worrying for a while and, as we shall see, may go for many years before discovering that there is a name like migraine or allergy to assign to their experience and that there are definite modes of treating the complaint.

Some of the patients said they expected the physician to be honest in the face of uncertainty. The matter of verity is, of course, a very complex one, for if the physician were absolutely honest about his uncertainty he would no doubt demoralize his patients. The factor involved is what appears to be honesty to the patient, not absolute blurting honesty. It is possible that the upper-middle class patient, in particular, appreciates an occasional ritual admission from his physician that "nobody really knows much about this"[1] and that the lower class patient appreciates a statement of uncertainty followed by tests or specialist consultation "just to make sure," the tests or specialty consultation being a mode of obtaining certainty.

If the prescribed treatment after diagnosis seems to require frightening or noxious experience, the patient pays particular attention to instances where the physician has managed to *avoid* treatment. The physician in the first case history who tried to avoid sending the children to the hospital is one example of what is admired. More strictly relevant to competence, however, are instances where the patient believed surgery to be necessary—as in "appendicitis," for example. The physician is considered extraordinarily "good" if he manages to cure without surgery, though not "bad" if he must use it. None of the patients interviewed could bring himself to accept surgery of even a commonplace sort, unless he felt that all other possibilities had been thoroughly explored. Avoiding surgery brings not only gratitude but also a belief in exceptional competence.

[1] See the "Alas, we don't know" type. Potter, Stephen, *op. cit.*, p. 19.

Finally, in this brief examination of the way in which patients evaluate their experience in the course of medical consultation and treatment, it is necessary to mention the way the patient looks at the "cure" of his illness. Assessment of cure is, of course, one that varies with the patient's beliefs, for while one may believe that a physician cured his cough by prescribing a cough syrup, another may believe that a physician merely made him comfortable while the cough ran its appointed course. Indeed, the critical patient might insist that he would be free of his symptoms at about the same time whether or not he consulted a physician, and in this sense might deprecate the physician's efforts entirely.

However, all the patients who discussed "cure," no matter how sophisticated, assumed that a "good" doctor should actively intervene in illness. It is intervention, even if it is only naming the illness or prescribing apparent palliatives, that seems to demonstrate to the patient that the physician is "really" working on the case and doing something about the illness. Activity for its own sake seems to be required, as is implied in the following lower-middle class woman's complaint:

> My daughter had a virus of some kind once and I got the doctor over and he just looked at her and shrugged. He said, "It's just a virus of some kind. Keep her in bed and let her get plenty of rest and she'll get over it. There's not much else to be done." But it dragged on and on, and while it did clear up finally, I felt I didn't get very good treatment. [Interviewer: Why not?] Well, I felt he wasn't very interested. He didn't examine her very thoroughly, and he should have been working at finding a cause instead of just letting it go. He should have been making tests when it dragged on so long.

In a vague sort of way, there seems to be implicit in this complaint some timetable[1] of cure, some notion of the "reasonable" amount of time after which, should symptoms continue, suspicion arises that all is not well.

[1] Unpublished material by Julius A. Roth on the idea of a timetable in the behavior of tuberculous patients is relevant here as is Fred Davis' "Definitions of Time and Recovery in Paralytic Polio Convalescence," *American Journal of Sociology*, vol. 61, May, 1956, pp. 582–587.

# 3. Patient Attitudes Toward Medical Practice

THE PRECEDING CHAPTER showed that the patients used two criteria—technical competence and personal interest—to evaluate their experience with medical care. These are what they want from medical care. In this and the succeeding chapter we will ask how in the patients' eyes the three kinds of practice give them what they want, and how perception of "competence" and "interest" is contingent upon the way in which these practices are organized.

First, however, it seems wise to recall the peculiarities of these patients. They have had highly atypical experience with a relatively rare kind of medical practice and so are more sophisticated than the average patient. All of them were enrolled in the Medical Group at the time of the study—those who were dissatisfied enough to drop out earlier provided none of the data. And, finally, simple economic advantages accrue to the subscribers to the prepaid medical group practice. These potential biases should be kept in mind when considering the patients' evaluations.

## "Personal Interest" in Entrepreneurial and Group Practice

Our patients tend to believe that the entrepreneurial practitioner is likely to take more personal interest in them than would practitioners in the Medical Group. The Montefiore Medical Group survey turned up some evidence supporting this conclusion. When the patients were asked, "Does it seem to you that on the whole the doctors in HIP are more interested in you than the doctors you had before you joined HIP?" 41 per cent of those responding answered that HIP and non-HIP doctors were about the same in their interest. Twenty-five per cent answered that HIP doctors were more interested in them, and 30 per cent answered that non-HIP doctors were more interested in them. (Four per cent had no opinion.) This small difference hardly supports the above assertion, but it becomes somewhat more convincing when we eliminate the responses of the 35 per cent of subscribers who reported no regular doctors before joining HIP[1] (and who thus are not in a position to make any such comparison): 38 per cent of the 412 remaining assert the greater interest of their prior entrepreneurial practitioner compared to 23 per cent asserting the greater interest of their HIP physicians.

More evidence is to be found in responses to the question, "Did you or your wife or husband ever have an experience with a doctor when you felt you were *insulted?*" "Insulted" is a strong word, and, as expected, few answered, "Yes." But while 2 per cent answered, "Yes," for "a non-HIP doctor only," and an additional 2 per cent for "both HIP and non-HIP doctors," 12 per cent indicated that they felt they were insulted "by a HIP doctor only." Furthermore, when asked, "Some people say the Montefiore Group has a clinic atmosphere that makes them feel they are charity cases. Do you agree?" 15 per cent of those responding answered, "Yes, very much"; 38 per cent answered, "Yes, a bit."

Finally, we may note that different practitioners in the Medical Group are not all viewed as equally interested. Of those who have made use of their present Montefiore Medical Group

---

[1] A sample survey of New York residents found that 40 per cent had no "family doctor." See the Committee for the Special Research Project in the Health Insurance Plan of Greater New York, *Health and Medical Care in New York City*, Harvard University Press, Cambridge, Mass., 1957, p. 58.

The problem of defining "family doctor" and asking the proper question of respondents in order to determine whether they have one or not is severe and may explain the wide variation in findings. Odin W. Anderson and Paul B. Sheatsley, in *Comprehensive Medical Service* (Health Information Research Series, no. 9, 1959, p. 53) found that of a special sample of HIP enrollees, 23 per cent reported no family doctor of their own. Of a matched sample of New York City enrollees in another insurance plan, 11 per cent reported no family doctor.

Two national sample surveys may also be cited for comparison. The NORC-HIF survey (see footnote on p. 35) found that only 19 per cent had no regular doctor. Another survey found that 18 per cent of a national sample had no regular doctor. See Gaffin, Ben, and Associates, *What Americans Think of the Medical Profession* (pamphlet available from the American Medical Association, n.d.), p. 1.

Family Doctor (N = 584), 16 per cent felt he does not "take as much interest in [them] as he should." Of those who have young children and have made use of their present Montefiore Medical Group pediatrician (N = 201), 13 per cent felt there was a lack of interest. But of those who have used the other Montefiore Medical Group specialists (N = 482), 23 per cent felt there was a lack of interest. Given the organization of the Medical Group and the more fleeting formal and technical nature of the specialist-patient relationship, this difference makes sense.

To sum up, we may say there is consistent evidence from answers to a variety of questionnaire items that many patients believe the Montefiore Medical Group is more deficient in the quality of personal interest than the solo practices they have known. Thus, it seems contradictory to note that only 7 per cent of the patients reported themselves "generally *dis*satisfied with the care [they have] gotten at Montefiore."[1] Forty-seven per cent said they were "completely satisfied," and 46 per cent reported that they had "some complaints but [were] generally satisfied." It is clear from the interviews that there is no real contradiction: the patients' satisfaction is real enough but practical in character and limited in expectation. Furthermore, the interviews provide evidence to suggest that at least some of their evaluation of the Medical Group is a function of their response to the way its services are organized.

Of the 36 families visited, the adult members of 25 families either had no regular relation with an entrepreneurial physician before joining HIP or had experiences with solo practitioners that seriously offended or frightened them. Four liked their former physicians but felt no commitment to them. Only seven of the 36 families manifested a strongly positive response to their former physician.[2] In spite of the fact that the adults of less than a third of the families had both extensive and satisfying experience

---

[1] The Montefiore Medical Group is among the half-dozen HIP medical groups with the *lowest* rate of patient complaints.

[2] In comparison, in the Montefiore Medical Group survey of subscribers, 27 per cent were "sorry to leave their regular non-HIP doctors" upon joining HIP. Eighteen per cent answered that they were not sorry because they "kept him anyway." Twenty per cent said that they were not sorry to leave him, and 35 per cent answered that they had no regular doctor before joining HIP.

with solo medical practice, the adults in all of these families expressed the belief that they were more likely to obtain personal interest from a fee-for-service physician in his neighborhood office than from a "prepaid" physician in his Medical Group office.

In searching for reasons to justify this belief, many of the patients referred to the organization of practice. For one thing, the mere fact of being in a prepaid plan—of paying in advance as it were—was brought up to explain this feeling. This is one of the connotations of the word "charity" as some patients use it: that the medical service is prepaid and they are not expected to take out a few banknotes at the end of the consultation, leads to a sensitivity to getting services "free" and therefore on a "charity" basis. For example, a patient said, "I felt I was a charity patient." Then he was asked, "What do you mean?" and he answered, "Well, I felt I was a free patient, that the doctors don't care about us because we are free[1]."

Another way of thinking negatively about prepayment involves the idea of being a captive patient whom the physician never need worry about. Some patients felt that in fee-for-service practice the physician is stimulated to be attentive and interested by the fact that he has not yet been paid for his services and that he can "lose" his patient if he does not satisfy him. In this sense, patients felt that prepayment leads the Medical Group physician to take his patients for granted because they have paid him in advance.[2]

To the fact of prepayment we may add the fact of rationalization and bureaucratization of services. The existence of many consulting-rooms, many secretaries, nurses and other personnel not directly involved in consultation, many patients waiting to

[1] In a study of HIP physicians, McElrath found that they attempt to justify their HIP practice by describing it as "charity" work. In this sense the patients' sensitivity seems to have a very real basis in fact. See McElrath, Dennis C., "Prepaid Group Medical Practice: A Comparative Analysis of Organizations and Perspectives," unpublished Ph.D. dissertation, Yale University, 1958.

[2] If the prepayment contract is problematic for the patient, it seems no less problematic for the physician, since it allows no way of getting rid of objectionable patients beyond passing them on from Family Doctor to laboratory to specialists and back again. Some evidence was gathered to suggest that the physicians, at least in moments of depression, also feel captive to their prepaid patients.

see their doctors, even the sense of efficiency—all this communicated a certain lack of intimacy, as is indicated in the following quotation:

> I guess you wait about the same time you have to wait in a private doctor's office, but you feel you're on a conveyor belt when you get in there.

Bureaucratization is thus expressed by the recurrent phrase "clinic atmosphere," and the negative connotation is compounded by the fact that the word "clinic" to these patients means public or free, and therefore, a self-demeaning source of medical care. The missing sense of intimacy becomes, through the word "clinic," connected anew with the "charity" connotation induced by prepayment.

Another source of complaint is the particularly high turnover of physicians. Thus, every patient who brought up the matter of tenure thought rapid turnover to be a deficiency. Some were merely annoyed at having to repeat their histories to new doctors. Others, like the patient quoted below, felt that lack of a long-term physician implied lack of opportunity to develop a personal relationship:

> When you keep having different doctors, they never get a chance to really know you and when they don't know you well, you can't expect them to be able to give you the kind of attention and interest you'd like.

While in a technical sense physicians with the same qualifications are interchangeable in a plan of treatment—the concept of standard interchangeability underlying any cooperative, rather than solitary, mode of practice—the sense of personal interest is predicated on a long-term relationship of familiarity that is built up between noninterchangeable individuals.

All that has been discussed thus far refers not to the qualities of doctors but to the suspicion that irrespective of whatever individual variation exists, the organized circumstances of practice apply systematic pressures that affect the doctor-patient relationship. By the very fact of being served by a prepaid, centralized medical group, some patients will expect to find in the doctors they consult only a minimum of personal interest; by the very nature of a solo, fee-for-service, neighborhood practice, they expect to find personal interest.

### "Competent Care" in Entrepreneurial and Group Practice

While the patients believe that solo practice is likely to encourage a doctor to take personal interest in them, they also tend to believe that neighborhood practice is unlikely to provide as adequate medical care as the group practice. This was revealed when patients were asked what sort of practice they would choose if money were no object. One answered, "It's hard to decide. I guess I'd choose a private doctor, but then you have to consider that HIP has specialists right there and you can get all those tests there." The centralized, rationalized, somewhat impersonal medical group has some advantages.

But those advantages do not seem to be a function of the individual doctors involved. In the survey of Montefiore Medical Group subscribers, the results indicated that most patients do not believe group physicians are any more competent as individuals than entrepreneurial physicians. One question asked, "Did you or your wife or husband ever have a doctor who seemed to be *incompetent?*" Exactly the same proportion—10 per cent—answered, "Yes, a HIP doctor" as answered, "Yes, a non-HIP doctor." Another question asked, "Does it seem to you that on the whole HIP doctors are *better doctors* than the ones you had before joining HIP?" Much the same proportion—13 per cent—answered, "Yes, HIP doctors are better" as the proportion—10 per cent—which answered, "Yes, non-HIP doctors are better." Fifty-five per cent felt they were both about the same and 22 per cent answered that they didn't know.

Although most patients therefore see little difference in ability between the physicians of both systems, many do think there is some difference in the medical care they get from them. Asked, "Do you think that on the whole you've gotten *better medical care* from the Montefiore Medical Group than you got from the non-

HIP doctors before you belonged to HIP?" only 13 per cent answered "No, got better medical care from non-HIP doctors. In contrast, 45 per cent answered, "Yes, got better medical care from Montefiore Medical Group," 31 per cent feeling both were about the same, and 11 per cent saying that they "don't know." The difference is about as great when we eliminate from tabulation subscribers who had no regular doctor prior to joining HIP, for of the 424 remaining, 43 per cent felt they got better medical care from the Montefiore Medical Group, compared to the 16 per cent who felt that they got better medical care from the non-HIP doctors they had previously.[1]

In arriving at their conclusion about the superiority of the Montefiore Medical Group, the patients who were interviewed mentioned a variety of things. Running through many explanations was the criterion of having ready access to routine use of a variety of technical facilities. Some patients differentiated between entrepreneurial physicians on this basis, as the following statement of a lower-middle class woman indicates: "He was a fine doctor; he had an office on Park Avenue. . . . I had great faith in him—after all, he had his own x-ray machine, you know, and he has some lab technicians working for him there too." Even more patients, however, used this criterion to compare the Medical Group with solo practice. They felt that a medical center in which a variety of physicians and technical facilities are available is more likely to be able to give them "good" medical care than a neighborhood office. As one lower-middle class male put it,

> They have all those tests and x-rays there, you know, and if you have to see a specialist, he's right there. If there's a real emergency, you can get an x-ray the same day, and you can see a specialist. When I had my private doctor, I had quite a time getting some tests I needed and seeing a specialist.

[1] Compare this with the findings in Simon, N. M., and S. E. Rubushka, *A Trade Union and Its Medical Service Plan*, Labor Health Institute, St. Louis, 1954, p. 18; 27 per cent of a sample of subscribers felt they got better care at the Labor Health Institute than "outside," 35.5 per cent felt they got the same, and 5.5. per cent felt that the care was inferior.

Paradoxically, while the patients think prepayment encourages a "charity attitude," they also think it encourages technically superior care. They believe that it allows them access to diagnostic facilities and yet protects them from commercial motivation on the part of the physician. When the independent, fee-for-service practitioner refers the patient to others for tests, or for consultation, this will cost the patient money, and can thus elicit reluctance or even suspicion on the part of the patient who does not feel very sick. One patient complained, "I think he had money to make when he sent me around to this place for tests and to that specialist." In contrast, another felt that solo practitioners may have too much regard for the patient's pocketbook, and so avoid recommending possibly valuable tests—"The private doctor is afraid to send a patient to a specialist because he knows the patient's going to complain about having to pay that extra amount." Either way, solo fee-for-service practice is seen to lack the impetus to provide "proper" technical and consultative resources, whether it is motivated by venal considerations or by conscientious concern with the economic burden of the patient.

The prepaid medical group plan, on the other hand, is viewed as free from these considerations. As a rather suspicious man said, "In HIP they don't make any money when they send you to a specialist, or have you take a test, so you can have more confidence in them." Further, the principle of prepayment is seen to encourage patients to use medical services early and quickly enough to imply that illness may be caught in more hopeful stages than would be the case otherwise. As one patient said, "When you have a private doctor you never drop in, you never call him unless you have something wrong right away, and it has to be serious, otherwise you'd treat it yourself and let it drag on. You'd think twice before making a three dollar visit." Thus, the centralized medical group practice marshalls technical, diagnostic, and consultative resources that make for "good" medical care, and the prepayment principle allows those resources to be used freely and with honest intent. It seems to be these assumptions rather than belief in the superiority of the group physicians as individuals that lead the patients to ascribe a better technical

quality of medical care to the Medical Group than to entrepreneurial practice.

## Convenience in Entrepreneurial and Group Practice

Thus far we have acted as if most of the patient's behavior is
guided by his judgment of the technical and interpersonal
quality of medical care. Apparently this is not true of most
patients most of the time: their experiences with medical care
tend to be casual and are treated in a casual manner, not in a
mood of calculating with fear the chances of life and death. It
appears to be in part the belief that the illness suffered (like a
cold) is not serious and in part belief that for minor illness any
doctor is technically competent which sustains the casual character of most medical experience. For most people medical
experience is an unimportant part of everyday life in which there
is little anticipation of the life-and-death drama communicated
by popular books, magazines, movies, and television programs.
Indeed, this is also true for the physician himself, and as much of
a problem of "good" practice lies in the deadly routine of treating
minor complaints as in the technical education and skill of the
physician.

Most people would much rather see a television program than
a doctor. Unless they are in discomfort or suspect a serious illness,
they want to spend as little time with medical care as possible.
Symptomatic of this is frank expression in the interviews of a
desire to have medical services arranged as conveniently as possible. "Convenience" is, of course, involved not only in what
patients consider to be their routine needs—there, it is simply a
desire to get consultation over with as quickly as possible, so as
to be able to get home for supper, or for a favorite television
program—but also in emergencies where easy and quick access to
a physician may save a life.

It is most often physical and temporal accessibility that
stimulates complaints and difficulties in these patients' interviews, and, in fact, it seems to be the selfish convenience of the
patient that is among the things involved in the wistful mythology

of the "oldtime family doctor." One woman contrasted her "old" doctor with the entrepreneurial practitioner she had before joining HIP as follows:

> Thirty years ago we had a family doctor who was just wonderful. He understood us, he explained everything to me I asked about, and he really sent us small bills. But I resented the doctor we got after the old one died. He didn't explain anything, he had you in and out of the office in a flash. He was so busy he wouldn't do anything for you unless you were really sick.

So far, this fits into our analysis of "personal interest." But when that woman and her husband were asked whether, if money were no object, they would rather remain in the Medical Group or have an entrepreneurial doctor, the element of personal convenience emerged in a happy little fantasy.

> HUSBAND:   Well, I suppose if I were a millionaire, or half a millionaire, why I guess it'd be handier to have my own doctor.
>
> WIFE:   Well, why don't you have your own private doctor like President Eisenhower?
>
> HUSBAND:   Yeah, that's a real good idea. He'd come and see me once a day to ask me how I felt, and if anything was wrong, I'd tell him and he'd take care of it.
>
> INTERVIEWER:   Yeah, and he can give you a shave too.
>
> HUSBAND:   Yeah (Laughs).

What is significant about the fantasy is that it emphasizes the belief that an entrepreneurial practitioner may be more plastic to the patient's convenience. The patient may, if he had the money and the right doctor, find in the doctor a body servant, or at least someone in constant servile attendance such as has occurred in the past in the case of royalty, or even merely well-to-do Victorian families. The Medical Group is not seen to be so potentially flexible.

But, recalling the condition of money being no object, and assuming the condition, even in The Bronx, of a seller's rather than a buyer's market in the merchandising of medical care, the reality of entrepreneurial practice reported by the patients is not so happy as the fantasy might imply. The subscribers were asked to reply to this request: "Here are some things patients have complained about in HIP. Please check the one most important complaint that you agree with." They were also asked to reply to this: "Some patients have made some of the same complaints about non-HIP medical practice. Please check the one most important complaint about non-HIP doctors that you agree with." Thirty-five per cent of the subscribers checked, "Waiting for the doctor even when I have an appointment" as their complaint about HIP, and 43 per cent checked it for entrepreneurial practice.[1] Twenty-nine per cent of the subscribers checked "Feeling that the doctor's rushing me in and out of the office" for HIP and 24 per cent checked it for entrepreneurial practice. Six per cent of the subscribers checked "Can't get house-calls" for HIP, and 24 per cent checked it for entrepreneurial practice.[2] Of noncomparable items, 14 per cent agreed with the complaint about HIP practice, "Can't keep the same doctor, they change so often." Only 3 per cent agreed that entrepreneurial practice was "Too expensive." Other complaints were scattered, and few subscribers agreed with each other about them with the single exception of the physical and temporal inaccessibility of HIP practice—7 per cent wrote in complaints about inconvenience. Clearly, in these complaints entrepreneurial practice fares little better and sometimes much worse than group practice.

[1] The questions asked and the manner of asking were not the same, but we might note the following: (1) In the NORC-HIF survey, 45 per cent of the national sample agreed that it is true that "doctors make you wait entirely too long when you try to see them in their office." (2) In the Gaffin survey (*op. cit.*, p. 4) 41 per cent of the national sample agreed that it is true that most "doctors keep people with appointments waiting longer than necessary," though only 15 per cent agreed this to be true of their own doctors; (3) a limited sample of HIP subscribers in New York contained only 20 per cent agreeing that doctors "make you wait entirely too long." See Anderson, Odin W., and Paul B. Sheatsley, *op. cit.*, p. 63.

[2] Comparison is again difficult, but the evidence seems to be that there is much national dissatisfaction with house-calls. (1) The NORC-HIF survey found that 44 per cent of a national sample reported that they would have "a great deal" or "a little trouble getting a doctor to come to [their] home at night or on a Sunday." (2) In the Gaffin study (*op. cit.*, p. 4) 51 per cent agree that most doctors are "hard to reach for emergency calls," 19 per cent agreeing that this is true of their own doctors. (3) Earl Koos in " 'Metropolis'—What City People Think of Their Medical Services" (in *Patients, Physicians and Illness*, edited by E. Gartly Jaco, The Free Press, Glencoe, Ill., 1958, p. 114) found that 51 per cent of his sample criticized physicians' reluctance to make house-calls; (4) Anderson and Sheatsley (*op. cit.*, p. 63) report that of their HIP sample 18 per cent agree that they have trouble getting house-calls.

### The Family Health Maintenance Demonstration, the Montefiore Medical Group, and Entrepreneurial Practice

Thus far we have seen that Montefiore Medical Group subscribers tend to feel that "personal interest" is lacking in the Medical Group as compared to entrepreneurial practice, but that they get better medical care in the Montefiore Medical Group than they got from entrepreneurial practice. Interviews also suggested that they believed that patients were more likely to get convenient care from an entrepreneurial practitioner than from the Medical Group, even though most of those interviewed did not appear to have obtained convenient care from solo practitioners in the past. What is the position of the Family Health Maintenance Demonstration in these evaluations? Designed to be positively attractive to patients, but organized within the familiar Montefiore Medical Group setting on an unfamiliar team basis, how was it compared with the other modes of practice?

First, there was an overwhelming expression of satisfaction with the Demonstration. All but one of those responding to a questionnaire administered while the Demonstration was still in existence answered, "Yes" to the question, "On the whole, have you liked being a member of the Demonstration?" The vast majority of those responding also felt that they were getting better medical care from the Demonstration—96 per cent felt it was better than that received when they were "regular" HIP subscribers, and 84 per cent felt it was better than that received from their prior entrepreneurial practitioners. However, the Demonstration was considered superior to each of the other forms of practice in different ways. The "one most important thing about the kind of medical care . . . gotten in Family Health that . . . [was] not gotten in regular HIP" was, for 72 per cent of the respondents, "personal interest." But the "one most important thing about the kind of medical care . . . gotten in Family Health that . . . [was] not gotten . . . from private practice" was, for 68 per cent of the respondents, "enough tests and examinations."

In a followup questionnaire administered a year after the Demonstration was terminated (two and a half years after the above-mentioned questionnaire) much the same results were obtained, even though somewhat different questions were used. Former Demonstration patients were asked, "How do you feel Family Health compares with regular Montefiore HIP care in its effect on the general health of you and your family?" Ninety-two per cent of those responding checked, "More likely to be healthy as a Family Health patient." Asked, "How do you feel Family Health compares with the private medical care you have had in its effect on the general health of you and your family?" 85 per cent checked, "More likely to be healthy as a Family Health patient." Further, they were asked, "Most of you seem to have found it pleasant to be a patient in the Family Health Maintenance Demonstration. How does the Demonstration compare in pleasantness with regular Montefiore HIP care?" Ninety-four per cent found it "more pleasant to be a Family Health patient." And when asked, "How does the Demonstration compare in pleasantness with the private medical care you have had?" 74 per cent answered it was "more pleasant to be a Family Health patient."

It seems quite clear that those who have experienced the Demonstration, with its uniquely organized team services, believe it to offer the virtues without the deficiencies of both the Montefiore Medical Group practice and of entrepreneurial practice. Not as overwhelmingly, but significantly nonetheless, many of the patients felt that this mode of giving medical care had done something additional for them. In the earlier questionnaire they were asked, "Do you think the Demonstration has uncovered things wrong with you that you didn't know before?" Twenty-nine per cent answered, "Yes," 58 per cent, "No," and 13 per cent, "Don't know." But while about one in four felt that previously *unknown* conditions were discovered, about one in two felt that previously *untreated* conditions were treated for the first time. Asked, "Do you think the Demonstration has treated you for things that were never treated before?" 47 per cent answered, "Yes," 47 per cent, "No," and 6 per cent, "Don't know."

In the followup questionnaire they were asked, "Do you think you and your family are in better health now than you were before entering Family Health?" Forty-two per cent answered, "Yes"; 50 per cent, "No, most of us about the same"; 1 per cent answered, "No, most of us probably worse"; and 7 per cent answered, "Don't know." Then they were asked, "Do you think that Family Health had much to do with the general health of you and your family?" Thirty-nine per cent answered, "Yes, it improved our health"; 50 per cent answered, "While it hasn't improved it, it has prevented our health from becoming worse"; 7 per cent answered, "No, had little effect"; 4 per cent answered, "Don't know"; and none answered, "Made our health worse."

Thus, not only did most of these patients feel that the virtues, without the deficiencies of both Montefiore Medical Group and entrepreneurial practice, were embodied in the Demonstration, but a good proportion of them also felt that it had a positive effect on their well-being. Whether or not it has indeed had such effect is a matter for medical assessment, and is discussed at length in another book.[1] How the patients arrive at such a conclusion—no matter whether it is true or false—is a matter for sociological assessment. We turn now to an attempt to suggest what aspects of the Demonstration, within the framework of patient attitudes that we have described, contribute to the patients' evaluations.

[1] A forthcoming volume by George A. Silver, *The Family Health Team*.

# 4. The Family Health Maintenance Demonstration

THUS FAR WE HAVE DISCUSSED in detail two kinds of practice and patients' responses to them. Each was seen by a significant number of patients to be lacking either in sufficient technical facilities or in personal interest. Many patients, however, seemed to feel that in a third practice, the Family Health Maintenance Demonstration, both prerequisites for good medical care were present. What was it about team practice of medicine in a prepaid medical group plan that stimulated their enthusiasm? In this chapter we shall attempt to indicate how professional tasks were performed in this third practice, and how the patients responded to them.

### A Sample Interview

We begin with a long segment of an interview with three Demonstration patients—a middle class Jewish husband, his wife, and his father. The views expressed in it are typical, though the participants were unusually articulate. The interview was tape recorded and literally transcribed. It has been edited sufficiently to make the meaning clear and preserve anonymity. At the time of the interview the family had already been discharged from the Demonstration and returned to regular Montefiore Medical Group care.

INTERVIEWER: What was the most pleasant thing about the plan?

WIFE: Well, I liked the people that I associated with, the nurses, and the doctors. . . . I found them very helpful. What's important is that . . . you have confidence in them; you feel that when you speak to them you know they're helping you. And

71

well, let's put it this way—when I had something to ask them I didn't feel as if I was asking something silly. You know, like some aches and pains that you feel might be imaginary. They listened and they helped you and that was that. . . .

INTERVIEWER:   Well, we don't have to go into names, but how did you like your HIP doctor before you went into Family Health?

HUSBAND:   We liked him very much. As a matter of fact, we asked to have him back again. We do have him back now that we've left Family Health.

WIFE:   The Family Health doctor was also a very charming person. . . .

INTERVIEWER:   What was extra in Family Health? In HIP there was a doctor you liked and you could talk to. . . .

WIFE:   Well to me it was more personal. It's difficult—

HUSBAND:   It's more as if he were your own family doctor on the outside, rather than . . . a clinic doctor. As you walk into HIP you sit down, you see all these people. It reminds you of a hospital clinic. However, when you have an appointment at Family Health, you have your own waiting-room. It was as though he were your own family doctor. He didn't have too many patients. He took time with you. He had the time to give you.

INTERVIEWER:   So the time is as important as his being—

HUSBAND:   That's right. While the doctors in HIP do not give you the rush act, you sort of know they have a schedule. But when you go to your own private doctor he takes more time—let's say he is building up a practice and that's part of the routine.

INTERVIEWER:   Well, what else about Family Health was so good?

WIFE:   Well, when my husband joined Family Health I was pregnant at the time, and the baby was born under Family Health. . . . The nurse was very nice and gave me many helpful hints. She came here in the morning, showed me how to bathe the baby, and dealt with any problems that I had. I mean, I felt no hesitation in calling on her. And believe me, I had a few problems. I felt that, well, as my husband said, it was a personal feeling. I didn't feel that I was taking up too much of their time—because I felt she was interested enough to want to help me in anything I would ask her. It was never too much trouble for her, on the phone, or if I happened to stop in at Family Health. She came here quite a few times to see how the baby was getting along, and helped out with the feeding schedule—you know, to make it easier for me. And I mean, I have always had a family doctor, for years. Before HIP. Oh, I've known him since I was about twelve I should say. I always felt free to call upon him and to talk to him—he always had time. And when I went into HIP I lost that feeling at the beginning, because I wasn't used to going into a large room, and sitting and waiting. Although I had to wait at my private doctor's office, it still wasn't the same. But then when I went into the Family Health I got that same feeling that I had with my family doctor originally. And they would call up occasionally, call up on the phone and ask me how the baby was doing or was there anything that bothered me, and I would tell them, well, let's say, about his tantrums and things like that, which I just didn't know too much about. They would tell me that it was nothing, it was a stage, or possibly he just wanted to get his own way. They'd tell me to just quiet him down, not to get angry at myself. And all those things have been very helpful to me. . . . And then, of course, the social worker—I felt many times that if I had any problems—like we'd be going out to the movies . . . the baby would go into screaming tantrums . . . we called her and the social worker told me that babies do try it, but I must explain to him—this was as he was getting older— that we did have a life of our own. We had to go out, but we were certainly coming back. And I tried it. I wouldn't say that it was always successful, but it did help. The association was always so pleasant . . . I mean, they didn't go over a certain line or anything like that, but they gave you a feeling that they were interested in everything you had to say to them. All your ideas and all your thoughts. And that means a lot. I met quite a few people who belonged to HIP and they left it.

INTERVIEWER:   How about . . . the social worker and the nurse. What do you think each one was there for?

WIFE:   Well, I know the nurse helped out the pediatrician with the children. And as I understand it, the social worker was there to help out in any family problems that might arise. . . .

INTERVIEWER:   You saw mostly the nurse, I take it?

WIFE:   Oh yes. Of course, I must admit that most of my problems were centered around small things. When the baby had a little infection I didn't want to bother the doctor about it, you know, it wasn't serious, there was no elevation in temperature. I would call the nurse and tell her. And she'd tell me what to do and tell me that if anything developed, if there was a temperature, then I could call the pediatrician. Sometimes just a little action would help me and if anything serious happened, then I would call the pediatrician. . . .

INTERVIEWER: How about you, Mr. Baker, what has your experience been? I imagine you've had less than your wife.

HUSBAND: Much less. The only time I saw them was when I didn't feel well, on rare occasions, or for my annual examination. And that, for me, was the best thing that I got out of HIP—the fact that they called you for your periodic examinations. And I may say that it is the best examination I have ever had. Ordinarily, when you go to your own neighborhood family doctor, he checks your heart, your pressure, looks at your eyes, ears, nose and throat, pats you around a little and that's the end of it. But when the Family Health doctor gave us an examination I thought it was quite thorough—the fluoroscope and having the chest x-ray, electrocardiograph, and lab work done, and having the ear, nose, and throat man examine me, and my eyes examined by the ophthalmologist. I know that I had a complete, one hundred per cent examination. When I walked out of there I knew that if anything was wrong with me, they'd find it.

INTERVIEWER: Did you ever have one in HIP, before Family Health?

HUSBAND: Yes, I did, and there, as I said, it was a routine examination where the doctor examined you in the office. As a matter of fact, it was before I transferred to the Montefiore [Medical] Group. I had an examination by some doctor in another group, and he gave me the routine blood-pressure type and I asked about a chest x-ray, and laboratory work. He said, "Well, you have to call this lab [which was something I never even heard of]. You have to make your own appointment there, and they don't take you in the evenings, you must go there during the day." I was working and I couldn't make it so I forgot about the entire situation. . . .

INTERVIEWER: What was your relation with the members of the staff of Family Health? Whom did you see the most?

HUSBAND: Only the nurse, primarily because she used to help out on my examination with the audiometer.

INTERVIEWER: Have you been having hearing trouble?

HUSBAND:   They found that I was losing out in the lower tones of my hearing.

INTERVIEWER:   You can hear me all right?

HUSBAND:   Oh, sure, I can hear all right, but it's just that I was having a little difficulty with the lower tones. . . . Ordinarily, in the average examination, you don't get that sort of a test with the audiometer. The person who is losing his hearing wouldn't know about it until probably it was too late to be corrected.

WIFE:   One thing more—my father-in-law was included by Family Health. You see, they took the entire family, even if there was a grandparent with the family. He was included. And due to them, it's, I mean, they've been wonderful to him. . . .

HUSBAND:   Well, here's a case where my father had diabetes. They were able to catch it, and through proper diet and periodic examination they've been able to curb it, so that he does not have to use insulin at all. And he feels fine. But it was only because of the examination that they were able to do this.

INTERVIEWER (To Father):   Were you taking insulin before, or did they discover the diabetes, Mr. Baker?

WIFE:   Oh, no, he knew about it before from the neighborhood family doctor. But he just told him to go on a diet. He didn't tell him anything in detail—just keep off starchy foods and things like that. He never gave him a diet or took too much interest in it, even though he was our family doctor. But when Dad came into the Family Health, they immediately put him on a twelve hundred calorie diet, and he lost, I think, fifty pounds, right? . . .

HUSBAND:   The nurse, she came here and watched and made sure that the weight was going down steadily.

INTERVIEWER (To Father):   How did you like the nurse, Mr. Baker?

FATHER:   Oh, I liked her very much, she's a very nice little girl. I liked them all there, everyone. . . .

WIFE:   They're pleasant, and they're very charming. Let's put it this way, that they don't seem like medical people. . . .

INTERVIEWER:   As I understand it then, first, you felt you got better medical care, at least through these examinations.

HUSBAND:   Absolutely.

INTERVIEWER:   And, second, it was pleasant.

WIFE:  Which is important I think. It leads up to confidence in someone. And not that I don't have confidence in my HIP Family Doctor, don't misunderstand me. But it was a closer group of people. . . .

INTERVIEWER:  Well, what is the most crucial part of the program for you, given the fact that you're going to have to cut some of it out? What do you feel would be most dispensable? . . .

WIFE:  Well, as I said, I feel that the doctor was important, but I felt that the personnel were more important.

INTERVIEWER:  So in other words you would take someone like your regular HIP Family Doctor, with the same feeling of being rushed, as long as you would have the other two? Of the two, who was more important?

WIFE:  Well, to me, the nurse, because I was in closer contact with her than I was with the social worker. I mean, I asked a lot of questions about the baby and she helped. I discussed his sleeping habits with her a great deal. Being a nurse she was able to help me. And I used to come in and talk to her quite often in the afternoon. . . . She was always interested in how the baby was getting along. . . .

INTERVIEWER:  You mentioned this allergy business. Did you have, in looking back over the thing, any allergic reactions before?

WIFE:  Well, I thought I had a perpetual cold. Oh, this was going on for years. But I never paid too much attention to it, and I never inquired about it.

INTERVIEWER:  You had never consulted a doctor about it?

WIFE:  No, not until I came into Family Health. And they decided that it couldn't be a perpetual cold—it was ridiculous, I mean you do get colds . . . during the summer, but not continuously. And then they suggested that I see the allergist. After taking the scratch tests, he found I was allergic to feathers, to wool, to weeds, to anything that's in the air, practically speaking. And I've been taking these injections. And it helped me a great deal.

INTERVIEWER:  Did you have this allergy when you had your family doctor, before joining HIP?

WIFE:  I probably did, but as I say, I never paid much attention to it. It didn't even enter my mind that I was allergic to anything. I know that the average person is allergic to dust, I mean, that's natural. When you're dusting a room you will sneeze, and that's as far as I went. And I never bothered about anything else.

INTERVIEWER:    How did this come up in Family Health? Did you think it important enough to mention?

WIFE:    Well, I don't remember exactly, but it was right at the beginning, when we got into Family Health.

HUSBAND:    Perhaps at the first physical examination.

WIFE:    I said, "A stuffy nose," I don't know how it came about, but I had mentioned the fact that I found it hard to breathe and I always had to have Kleenex with me; and I couldn't understand why. And then my husband mentioned, "She thinks she has a perpetual cold all year round." They said it couldn't possibly be that, and that's when they suggested that I see the allergist.

In this interview the primary emphasis is on the interest which the patient feels is characteristic of the Demonstration. That interest is compared to what the old family doctor offered his patient in the happy though varnished past. Exploring the sense of interest is a task that will lead us into discussion of the staff of the Demonstration. Beyond interest, emphasis is placed on the technical adequacy of the program; this will also be seen to be a partial function of the organization of the personnel.

## Personal Interest

From the first interview to the last the patients emphasized their gratification with the interest that they felt was being taken in them in the Family Health Maintenance Demonstration. The question is, What is it about the Demonstration that communicates personal interest? The answer appears to lie not only in the way the staff works, but also in the division of labor within the staff teams.

In entrepreneurial medical practice, the behavior of the doctor alone usually constitutes the crucial variable for the patient. The physician often has an aide, receptionist, or nurse working with him, but none of the interviewed patients made any spontaneous mention of such an assistant. They seem to have had relatively direct contact with their neighborhood doctors, using few significant intermediaries.

In the Montefiore Medical Group, on the other hand, we find spontaneous mention of receptionists, aides, and nurses, for at the Medical Group with its rationalization of services these workers assume importance by their role in organizing the flow of work and so mediating between patient and doctor. In one patient's experience with the Montefiore Medical Group, the receptionist was of great importance in determining her responses:

> I called Dr. Charles. And when I called, the secretary said that I couldn't see him for three weeks. I said, "But I'm sick now, I have to see him now, not in three weeks." I said, "In three weeks I could be dead." . . . She said, "Well, I'm sorry, I'll have to let you know." I said, "You can't let me know, I want to know now." I said, "I feel very badly. . . . You can give me an appointment for any time that's convenient for him that day." She said, "No, you can't see him in less than three weeks. He's tied up." . . . But I had no further trouble like that. [Interviewer: Did you have the same sort of emergency again?] No, no. Well, the other emergency, as I say, was an infection . . . I called up and the secretary said, "Well, I have to ask Doctor Fox if he can squeeze you in. I'll have him call you back." He called me back . . . and said, "Come down and let me look at it." And I went down and, of course, I waited; I expected to, there were other people who had earlier appointments. . . . But you see, *that* I didn't mind, it was just the way the girl told me that I couldn't see him for three weeks.

In discussing the "clinic" atmosphere of the Group many patients spoke of "cold" receptionists and "unsympathetic" and "sarcastic" nurses in the same breath as "cold, curt" doctors.[1] In turn, patients spontaneously mentioned their feeling of gratitude and pleasure when a receptionist or telephone operator showed interest and sympathy, or recognized their name and asked after the children or the progress of their most recent illness. These personnel are thus inextricably connected with the patients' conceptions of the care they receive: as agents through whom the patient must pass before he reaches the doctor, they can color the

[1] The Montefiore Medical Group survey of subscribers found that 90 per cent of the sample asserted that the nurses, receptionists, and telephone operators at the Medical Group are courteous and pleasant. Only 10 per cent had any complaint about them.

patient's relation to the doctor himself. So it is not fortuitous that patients spontaneously mentioned the secretaries or receptionists in the course of describing how much they liked the Demonstration, as in the following sample:

> And another thing. The secretaries have a lot to do with making Family Health so nice. They're so nice and interested in us, they take such an interest. I always felt they really were interested in how things were coming along when I called. They'd always ask how I was and ask about the kids and they were always sympathetic.

Second in the patient's experience is the physician. In the Demonstration many patients felt that they could spend time with the doctor without feeling rushed.

> When you walk in there he's not ready to get rid of you right away and he gives you a full, thorough examination.

Indeed, one patient even used to see the doctor as a weekly counselor. All patients felt free to ask questions about their health or illness.[1]

> I didn't get the idea I was being treated automatically. I got facts about myself that I always wanted before, but that I couldn't ever get. I'd been sort of intimidated by doctors before I joined Family Health. You know—I was afraid to ask them questions because I always felt they wanted to get me out of the office as soon as possible. But in Family Health, well, really, I got to learn about things I never asked for even.

The doctor's interest is also communicated by what patients defined as extra, unexpected solicitude. There is the matter of house-calls, about which one patient said:

> I think we can appreciate the fact that all you do is call the doctor and he says, "I'm coming over to you" even though we say, "Don't, I just want to ask you a question." I know that I personally don't want to take advantage of him. He always goes out of his way to give you private, personal attention.

[1] The NORC-HIF (see footnote on p. 35) survey found that 50 per cent of a national sample agreed that doctors "don't tell you enough about your condition; they don't explain just what the trouble is." Forty-four per cent answered "Yes" to the question, "If you had a chance to talk to a doctor for half an hour, at no cost to you, are there any things about your own health that you'd like to ask him?"

Another way the doctor demonstrates interest is by himself calling the patient to inquire about the course of an illness. Still another reported by a patient or two lies in the symbolic act of taking the side of the patient against the hospital in which he is confined.

However, it must be remembered that many patients, particularly those in the semi-skilled and skilled manual and lesser white collar occupations, seem to feel that they are imposing on the doctor by asking him many questions.[1] When patients limit the topics they would dare bring to a doctor's attention, they restrict the areas in which the doctor is able to demonstrate personal interest. The presence of the nurse and the social worker on the staff seemed to encourage patients to bring more to professional attention than would be the case otherwise. This is apparent in the comment of a semi-skilled worker:

> Well sure, I talked to the doctors, and I felt they did have a lot more time to spare than most doctors, but I didn't think I should bother a doctor with a lot of things that were bothering me. . . . There are a lot of things that a doctor don't want to be bothered with because he has so many more important things to worry about. . . . But I never felt they were too rushed to talk to me, or they didn't want to talk to me. . . . I just felt it was more natural to talk to the nurse or social worker.

In the course of their work, the nurse and social worker made the patient feel at home when he entered the waiting-room, for they were quick to greet him and always inquired about his affairs. Spontaneously chatting with a person who has approached him, the patient is less likely to feel rushed, no matter how many scruples he may have about "taking someone's time," than he would be in an office chatting with someone he has asked to see by appointment.

The nurse and the social worker are people of whom patients may ask many questions that they feel are either too minor to

[1] The NORC-HIF survey found that of 12 "reasons that people sometimes give us for not seeing a doctor when perhaps they should," the one the greatest proportion of a national sample agreed applied to them was, "I don't like to bother the doctor unless it's necessary." Forty-one per cent indicated that they had put off going to the doctor for that reason. This response is inversely related to education, occupational status, and income.

bother the doctor with, or of such a character that the doctor is ill-equipped to handle them. Indeed, these workers may be used to answer questions that the doctor himself may not have answered adequately.

> As a doctor, he sometimes doesn't understand things, and sometimes he'd say something that would worry us or make us feel bad, and the nurse would explain to us later just what the doctor meant; that he meant it for our own good, and he was very concerned that we should do the right thing for our health.

Many patients spoke, too, of unsolicited suggestions about diet and child-rearing they had obtained from the nurse and the social worker. Many were gratified by visits the nurse or social worker made to them when they were hospitalized.

> The nurse and the social worker visited me a lot when I was at the hospital. Especially the nurse—she asked me all about how they were treating me and whenever anything came up she'd tell the doctor about it. You know, when you're sick in bed and you can't move around, anybody coming in is welcome, and it was very nice to have people from Family Health coming in to see how I was getting along.

Their other services, such as routine posthospital house-calls, visiting the children's school, contacting agencies for medical or dental care for an indigent relative, trying to obtain low-cost housing for the patients, were also cited by the patients as behavior that indicated interest. A semi-skilled city worker summed up the case.

> The most important thing about the Family Health is the personal kind of treatment you get there. When you leave you leave, you know, with a good taste in your mouth. . . . You don't sit in a line and have them say, next, and nobody knows you from Adam.

## The Perception of Medical Adequacy

When people are sick they feel some anxiety about themselves. When their home and neighborhood remedies fail, they feel at the mercy of the medical workers. The desire that medical workers take an interest in them may reflect some purely irrational anxiety, but, as has already been observed, it is also connected with a plausible chain of reasoning: if doctors are interested in me, they are more likely to take the extra pains necessary for the best possible medical treatment.

In their response to the Family Health Maintenance Demonstration, the patients made that connection explicit. One said that she felt encouraged to bring in her problems inasmuch as the workers took an interest in her, and *because* she brought all those problems in to be treated, the care was better than that received in other programs of medical care. Some patients felt that they were getting "extra" tests not given in the Montefiore Medical Group—some even felt the routine examination was an extra— but on the whole, most did *not* feel that their doctors in Family Health were more skilled than those in the Medical Group.

Perhaps the sense of the matter was communicated when a patient said of the Montefiore Medical Group, "They take care of you and they just don't care," or when another said, "No, the medical care really isn't any better than it is in HIP, but in a way it is better because they take such an interest in you that you begin doing things about your health, like dieting, that always seemed too much trouble before." The patients felt that the tools and skills were the same in Family Health as in the Montefiore Medical Group, but that they were used in a "better" way.

Many patients mentioned that being reminded by the secretary to have their routine annual examinations impressed them as "wonderful." This is an obvious example of the kind of thing by which "interest" is expressed to them, and they responded to it with pleasure. In assessing the quality of their medical care, they singled out the thorough examinations they obtained, the conservative care in which much consultation and extra tests were suggested in order to "make sure," and the attention paid to all their complaints. Beyond this, many of the patients felt that the mere fact that the professional workers "knew" them, and that the turnover of doctors had not been as rapid as in the Medical Group, made for more efficient care and less irritating repetition of the history of their complaints.

## Accessibility

In many of the quotations above there are obvious references to the accessibility of the Demonstration. Accessibility was physically superior to that of the Montefiore Medical Group, in the sense that the patients felt they could always call up or even drop in and find counsel. In addition, both the physicians and the public health nurses were believed to be very free with house-calls during the daylight hours when they were on duty, going to see the patients rather than requiring them to come to the Medical Center. Part of this accessibility was gained by the comparatively light caseload of the physicians involved, and part no doubt was a function of the special motives stimulated in the staff by participation in a demonstration rather than in a routine program. Whatever its cause, the patients found it more convenient than the Medical Group practice.

## Experience of Diagnosis and Treatment

Even though few if any patients were fully aware of the implications, it seemed that the attention they received affected the course of diagnosis and treatment. The patients reported that they were encouraged to see the professional workers and discuss freely with them their difficulties, just as the professional workers were encouraged to listen closely. Attention seemed to extend even to cases that usually do not come to the attention of professional workers, as we see in the following report, in which solicitude was expressed and treatment urged for what the patient himself tended to treat quite casually:

Last week the secretary telephoned me to make an appointment for you [the interviewer] to come over, and while we were talking she said, "You sound a little hoarse, Mrs. Rogers, is there anything wrong?" And I said, "No,—well, yes—but it isn't very much. I have sort of a laryngitis." "Well," she said, "you ought to get that treated. Why don't I get hold of the doctor. He's right here, and why don't you talk to him?" I said it was only a minor thing, I didn't need to bother the doctor, but she went ahead and tried to get him.

Trivia must certainly be dredged up in the process of attending to such minor complaints, but here medicine has a mode of gaining access to, and treating, the most elusive symptoms of all—those the patient has accepted as part of his existence. Indeed, these symptoms tend not even to be defined as symptoms by the patient, but as idiosyncrasies or annoying but tolerable facts of life. Chronic indigestion, persistent colds, headaches, backaches, and nervousness are often accepted by the patient in this fashion, particularly after their significance has been shrugged off or deprecated by a physician or two in the past.

Here is an example of the way one symptom that had never before received medical attention was discovered by the nurse in an informal context and subsequently investigated:

> The wife had had headaches for a long time, both while she was under private medical care and while she was a HIP subscriber. She said, "I never thought of seeing my private doctor about the headaches, and I never had any routine physical examination before, so they never really came up. The only time I went to my private doctor was when I thought I was really sick, and I told him about the sickness, not the headaches." When asked what she did for the headaches she said she didn't do anything, but when asked about aspirin she said, "Oh, of course, aspirin, but it didn't do me much good since I had them all day anyway." After she went into the Family Health program she happened to mention casually to the nurse, "Oh, I have such a terrific headache." The nurse asked her how long she had had it, and when the wife indicated she'd had it off and on for some time the nurse suggested a checkup. The wife had had an examination by the internist and one by the ophthalmologist, both of which were largely negative. She did state, however, that the internist decided that her headaches might be connected with her obesity, and suggested dieting. Upon this recommendation the nurse made out a diet for her and supervised her efforts to lose weight. The wife claimed that her headaches did become less frequent and severe after she lost some weight, but after she left the Family Health program she regained her weight and the headaches returned.

Another patient, lower class in background, was discovered by the nurse on a routine call to have been in bed for a week with a "cold." He expressed unwillingness to bother the doctor about "just a cold," which turned out to be a severe allergic reaction.

On the whole, not many instances like these were mentioned by the patients. Most of their daily symptoms had received medical attention at one time or another as the patients themselves agreed in their questionnaire responses. What was much more common in the patients' reports is the extent to which they felt that *serious* attention had been given to symptoms that received only cursory attention before. Many patients, we may recall from the last chapter, emphasized this. A brief example may help here:

> Mrs. Quince has had migraine headaches for many years. When asked what sort of treatment she had received for them before she was in Family Health she said, "Well, I went to a lot of doctors, but I got very little help. They gave me aspirin, APC, and that sort of thing, but it didn't do me much good. When I joined HIP I got a thorough physical checkup, but nothing was turned up. Then in Family Health, I had the same sort of checkup and the doctor explained how the headaches are connected with being tense. And I never noticed it before, but it's true. When I get tense and something's bothering me, I get those headaches. So once I knew that, I tried to relax and my headaches did tone down quite a bit. . . . But no, they're not entirely gone.

Many instances like the above were reported by patients as evidence not only of the sort of interest that was taken in them but also as evidence of the high quality of care provided.

Much of what has been said in the immediately preceding pages depends for its salience on the actual medical accomplishments of the program itself. In his report on the Demonstration, Dr. George Silver has presented the medical and administrative results of attempts to measure positive changes in health on the part of the Demonstration patients. However, a problem as critical as knowing how to treat illness is knowing how to attract patients, encourage them to cooperate with the procedures necessary for diagnosis, and get them to follow the prescriptions of professional workers. From this point of view, the Demonstration appears to have been an eminent success: a very large proportion of the patients expressed rather elaborate enthusiasm for the program, and as Silver reported, made extensive but not excessive use of its services in general.

The use of Demonstration services, however, seemed to have been quite selective. Professional workers on the practicing team were not all utilized in the appropriate way, and the Demonstration itself was on occasion bypassed in favor of entrepreneurial practitioners. In spite of their enthusiasm for the program, many patients did not use its services in a professionally approved way. Examination of these defections is of obvious importance for realistic understanding of problems of organizing medical care, and the remainder of this book will concentrate on their description and analysis. Turning first to the selective utilization of the professionals engaged in the Demonstration teams, we shall have occasion to analyze the significance of the organization of professional roles within the Demonstration to the utilization of services. Later, when we turn to examination of the use of "outside" physicians, we shall have occasion to look more closely at the relation of the overall organization of the Demonstration and the Montefiore Medical Group to the utilization of services.

PART TWO

THE UTILIZATION OF HEALTH SERVICES

# 5. Choices Between Professions in a Health Program[1]

PART ONE OF THIS MONOGRAPH sketched the three systems of medical care with which the patients have come into contact, and described the way the patients evaluated and compared them. Both the quantitative and qualitative data showed that the patients who had experienced all three types of care were extremely enthusiastic about the Family Health Maintenance Demonstration; therefore, we could conclude by and large that the Demonstration stimulated a high degree of patient satisfaction.

However, all we know about the nature of the patients' satisfaction thus far stems from their verbal expressions of enthusiasm. This is obviously a rather superficial basis for understanding their relations with the health program and other professional practices. Does their enthusiasm lead them to do everything the practitioners suggest? Does it lead them to use all available services? Does it encourage loyalty to the program? These questions refer to patient *behavior* rather than patient *attitudes*. It is to an aspect of patient behavior that we now turn.

The behavior we will focus on is the use of professional services. We assume that one of the major aims of medical practice is to get the patient to see a doctor and to obey his prescriptions, and that this aim is a necessary condition for successful medical practice. It would follow from this that the choice and use of medical services are strategic points for analysis. In the present case it is particularly strategic to examine the differential use of

[1] Portions of this chapter have already been printed in Freidson, Eliot, "Specialties Without Roots: The Utilization of New Services," *Human Organization*, vol. 18, Fall, 1959, pp. 112–116. Reprinted by permission of the Society for Applied Anthropology.

services because use of one type of practice in preference to another can tell us as much about the influence of the organization of practice on patient behavior as the influence of patients' preferences.

In studying the utilization of services we face the problem of what constitutes "proper" use. In the Family Health Maintenance Demonstration, as we see in Table 1, there was comparatively low utilization of the social workers. What does this mean?

TABLE 1. PER CENT OF ALL PATIENTS SEEN PER YEAR BY FAMILY HEALTH MAINTENANCE DEMONSTRATION STAFF[a]

| Followup year[b] | Per cent of all patients seen by physician | Per cent of all patients seen by public health nurse | Per cent of all patients seen by social worker |
|---|---|---|---|
| First year of service (N=523)[c] | 99.6 | 96.2 | 74.8 |
| Second year of service (N=513) | 95.3 | 78.6 | 56.3 |
| Third year of service (N=508) | 96.2 | 71.9 | 54.3 |
| Fourth year of service (N=476) | 97.1 | 66.2 | 35.5 |

[a] In any single year a patient is counted only once, no matter how many times he has consulted the staff worker.

[b] "Followup year" refers to a full year of service rather than a calendar year. Since all patients did not enter or leave the program at the same time, their followup years could begin in any month and on any year from 1952 through 1954.

[c] Some patients did not remain in the program for the full four years, which explains the changing total number of patients.

To answer the question requires the assertion of some standard of "proper" utilization in the face of patient "need." Such a standard is arbitrary, since there is no professional or scientific agreement about many patient needs any more than there is agreement about the way needs can be satisfied by particular techniques or services. Arbitrary or not, however, some standard must be asserted before we have a point on which to balance reality.

Two standards are commonly used, more perhaps because of their practicality than their ultimate merit. One is absolutely and crudely quantitative—the more frequently a service is used, it asserts, the more likely are the patient's needs to be met. This standard has the virtue of simplicity and directness, but it has the vice of vanity in its assumption that no matter how little definite knowledge underlies it, a professional service will do more good or less harm than no service at all.

The other standard is qualitative, based on the clinical (that is, practical) judgment of the professional worker. On the basis of his complex understanding of both the patients and the services he provides, the professional worker estimates patient needs and judges whether patients are using available services appropriately. The virtue of this criterion is that insofar as only intuitive forms of knowledge are usually available, the professional worker is in the best position to assert that knowledge. Its deficiency lies in the extent to which professional workers disagree with each other, thereby throwing doubt on the validity of their judgments.

Both of these standards will be used in our discussion of the utilization of services in the Family Health Maintenance Demonstration. They are used because the purpose of this study is not to evaluate the propriety of utilization so much as the occasions on which professionally desired utilization did not occur. The standards are used here only to establish the existence of a practical problem for the medical program, not to judge either the patients or the professional workers.

## The Use of Services in the Family Health Maintenance Demonstration

Two criteria were used to establish that a practical problem lay in the role of the social worker in the Family Health Maintenance Demonstration. First, as we have indicated, the number of patients who used the three professional workers—physician, public health nurse, and social worker—varied greatly. Over the four full years of service the public health nurse served more people than the social worker. Second, in the opinion of the professional workers of the program, the social worker alone of the three was seriously underutilized. It was felt that a rather large proportion of the families manifested problems that required the counseling or referral which the social worker was professionally equipped to provide, but that many of the patients did not use her aid. The cause of underutilization of the social worker could not be seen to lie in the patients' unawareness of their problems. While a few did resist "recognizing" that they suffered for the psychological reasons suggested by the professional workers, most of them recognized that they had some sort of problem. For the difficulties they recognized, they sought the help of the physician and the public health nurse, not the social worker.

In the early days of the program it was decided that the patient would be allowed to choose any professional worker for help with "emotional problems." It was assumed that the chosen counselor could obtain proper guidance in his handling of the case from the other members of the team and from a consulting psychiatrist. But it soon became clear that very few of the patients seeking aid for "emotional problems" chose the worker best equipped by training to give such aid—the social worker. Because the social workers felt this to be an unfortunate situation, and because the physicians and nurses began to feel somewhat overworked, it was decided that every effort be made to refer to the social workers all patients with personal problems. It was generally agreed, however, that most referrals to the social workers were unsuccessful—the patients persisted in seeking help from the physician or the public health nurse. Thus, the problem of utilization was expressed in two ways—few patients spontaneously chose to consult a social worker, and few who were referred to her would follow through with the suggestion.

Resistance to the social worker was a general characteristic of the patient population as a whole. Of the Family Health Maintenance Demonstration patients interviewed, 45 recalled some occasion on which they used the services of the nurse, compared to 15 who recalled using the social worker. Thirty-two of the patients recalling utilization of the nurse expressed a strong positive feeling toward her, compared to four who expressed such a feeling toward the social worker. Five patients of those interviewed actively refused to see the social worker upon being referred, and 13 expressed antagonism toward her. In a survey of the total patient population, moreover, the husbands and wives of the participating families were asked which worker they would choose to dispense with if it were necessary to drop the services of either the nurse or the social worker. More than two-thirds of the 86 per cent who made a choice were more willing to dispense with the social worker than the nurse, less than a third choosing to dispense with the nurse rather than the social worker.[1]

With only two representatives of each profession involved, obviously personality differences between the staff members themselves could not be controlled, but a number of observations were made to support the contention that the role of the social worker in the program, not her personality or training, was critical to utilization. About the same proportion of patients responded positively or negatively to the nurse and the social worker of one team as to those of the other team. Of the interviewed patients, 23 mentioned occasions in which they used the services of the nurse of one team, while 22 mentioned occasions in which they used the nurse of the other. Sixteen expressed positive feelings toward one nurse and 16 toward the other. Eight mentioned use of one social worker and seven mentioned use of the other. Seven mentioned negative feelings toward one social worker and six toward the other. In the surveys no consistent or significant differences in response could be found between patients of one team and those of the other. Given the fact that the personality of one nurse was markedly different from (even antagonistic to) that of the other, that one nurse was antagonistic to her social worker teammate and the other cooperative, the remarkable uniformity of patient responses, no matter which team served them, seems to be more a function of the professional roles than of the incumbents of those roles.

## Patients' Views of Consultation

The official records show that the patients used the physician most, the nurse next, and the social worker least. The patients' own impression of their use of services was in accord with the

[1] The same question was included in two different questionnaires, one administered while the Demonstration was still in operation and the other about two years later, after all families had been discharged. The proportions of the responses to the question varied by only one per cent from one survey to the other.

records, for when they were asked to rank the professional workers by frequency of use, the mean rank order[1] of the staff was identical with the actual mean rank order of utilization. As summarized in Table 2, the same rank order of perceived utilization was manifested in the patients' answers to the questions, "To whom have you made the greatest number of visits for which you made an advance appointment?" and "Whom have you called on the phone [most] for one thing or another?"

TABLE 2. THE CONTEXT OF CONSULTING PROFESSIONAL WORKERS[a]

| Question asked | Mean rank order assigned by patients[b] | | |
|---|---|---|---|
| | Doctor | Public health nurse | Social worker |
| Whom have you used most often? | 1.6 | 2.8 | 3.5 |
| To whom have you made the greatest number of visits for which you made an advance appointment? | 1.0 | 2.3 | 2.6 |
| Whom have you called on the phone [most] for one thing or another? | 1.3 | 2.2 | 3.2 |
| With whom have you had the greatest number of informal chats about your affairs, chats *not* scheduled by appointments? | 2.6 | 1.7 | 2.4 |
| With whom have you been most friendly? | 1.8 | 2.2 | 3.1 |

[a] These questions come from two separate questionnaires, the number of respondents to each question fluctuating between 180 and 225. For simplicity, secretary rankings are omitted, as were rankings of the pediatrician.

[b] The patients were asked to assign the rank "1" to the person they have used most often or would choose first. Therefore, the smaller the average rank number, the more the patients assigning high priority to the staff worker.

In addition to questions about direct use, two questions were asked that were designed to determine the extent to which informal consultation took place. In answer to the question, "With whom have you had the greatest number of informal chats about your affairs, chats *not* scheduled by appointments?" the

[1] Statistically speaking, the mean rank order does not fulfill the requirements necessary for tests of the significance of the sort of responses presented here. It is, however, easily comprehensible for comparative purposes. Tests of significance of difference being inappropriate, none will be used. As a rough rule of thumb, however, a difference of .5 will be considered well worth noting.

nurse was ranked first, followed by the social worker and the physician. This ranking implies realistically enough that while the physician is indeed perceived to be used the most, he is used in a formal consultative role that is rather detached and distant. It is primarily the nurse who was seen in an accessible consultative role. However, in answers to the question, "With whom have you been most friendly?" the mean rank order of responses placed the physician first, but barely ahead of the nurse, and the social worker last. Here we may infer that the less accessible role of the physician does not preclude a sense of friendliness on the part of the patient any more than that the greater accessibility of the social worker induces friendliness.

## Patients' Conceptions of Staff Functions

The patients were also asked which worker they were most likely to use for a number of problems, ranging from purely technical medical problems to vague personal or social problems. They were asked whom they would choose to interpret the results of such tests as x-rays to them. Ninety-two per cent of them chose the doctor. When they were asked to assume their first choice to be unavailable, 82 per cent chose the nurse to interpret the results to them, 10 per cent the secretary, 5 per cent the doctor, and only 3 per cent the social worker. Thus, the doctor and the nurse were clearly identified with medical knowledge and competence, as we would expect, but the social worker was so completely separated from that area that she ranked below the secretary. This pattern was duplicated when the patients were asked to rank the personnel they would choose to call for advice about a cold too minor for a home-call or an office visit. As Table 3 indicates, the doctor was ranked first, the nurse second, the secretary to choose the proper professional person to give advice third, the secretary for her own advice fourth, and the social worker last, least likely to be called. This persistent pattern indicates that the social worker in the Family Health Maintenance Demonstration was perceived to be completely disengaged from the one problem area in our culture for which people are most likely to seek professional aid.

## TABLE 3. PATIENT IDENTIFICATION OF PROFESSIONAL FUNCTION[a]

| Question asked | Mean rank order assigned by patients[b] | | | | |
| --- | --- | --- | --- | --- | --- |
| | Physi-cian | Public health nurse | Social worker | Secre-tary to choose consultant | Secre-tary to give advice |
| If someone in your family had a cold too minor for a home-call or for coming in to Family Health, but you wanted to be sure you were doing the best you could, whom would you call for advice? | 1.3 | 2.1 | 4.5 | 2.8 | 4.1 |
| If you were having a problem getting one of the children to eat, whom would you call for advice? | 1.5 | 2.1 | 3.3 | 3.4 | 4.6 |
| If you were having a school problem with one of your children, whom would you call for advice? | 2.8 | 2.5 | 1.8 | 3.3 | 4.7 |
| If you were having a problem getting your children to go to bed, whom would you call for advice? | 2.1 | 2.3 | 2.7 | 3.2 | 4.7 |
| If you had trouble getting along with people, or difficulties in your marriage, whom would you be most likely to ask for help or advice?[c] | 1.9 | 2.5 | 2.0 | .. | .. |

[a] These questions come from two separate questionnaires, the number of respondents to each question fluctuating between 180 and 225.

[b] The patients were asked to assign the rank "1" to the person they have used most often or would choose first. Therefore, the smaller the average rank number, the more the patients assigning high priority to the staff worker.

[c] The secretary was not included as an alternative source of consultation in this question. The pediatrician was included in this question, but omitted here for simplicity.

Turning from obviously physical problems to the more ambiguous problems of child behavior—an area heavily emphasized in the program and on which the social workers concentrated their efforts—two questions were asked about problem areas that could be interpreted either medically or psychologically—trouble getting a child to eat and trouble getting a child to bed. In both instances the social worker was ranked third quite definitely in the case of eating (which implies an obviously physiological function) and somewhat more ambiguously for the problem of getting a child to bed. In the latter case the differences in ranking all three—doctor, nurse, and social worker—become narrow. For "a school problem with one of your children," the social worker definitely assumes first rank, but in the case of help for "trouble getting along with people" or "difficulties in . . . marriage," she shares first rank with the physician, the nurse trailing closely behind.

It is apparent that the more clearly physical the problem, the more definite are the patients about the rank order of people they would choose for advice. From physical problems the social worker is most definitely excluded. As the problems shift from eating to sleeping to school and personal affairs, however, the variety of patient choice increases and the social worker comes to assume more importance. This variety of choice is apparent in the range of differences between the mean rank orders of each problem, and the magnitude of each mean rank order itself. The greater the difference between adjacently ranked means, and the closer the first mean rank order to 1.0, the second to 2.0, and so on, as in the answer to the first question in Table 3, the more definite the agreement among the patients. Rescanning Table 3 with this in mind, we see that while the social worker was chosen more often first or second for school problems than any other members of the staff, there was no definite and clear consensus for this choice. The same may be said even more strongly for her near-first mean rank for "trouble getting along with people." While the patients are fairly definite about rejecting her from apparent medical affairs, they are not at all definite about accepting her for more social or psychological affairs even though many recognize the relevance of her role.

Obviously, answers to the questions may involve both knowledge and acceptance of who is supposed to be professionally qualified. Knowledge and acceptance, in fact, varies systematically by particular patient characteristics, as we shall see. But above and beyond what the patient brings to the Demonstration, there is also a reality which the Demonstration brings to him. Before dealing with systematic variation on the part of patients, it seems appropriate to discuss and analyze the organized roles of each of the professional workers in the Demonstration.

## The Physician[1]

The role of the physician was not much different from that of other physicians in the Montefiore Medical Group. The major deviation from the "normal" Medical Group role stemmed from the Demonstration physician's relatively light caseload, the evaluation and team consultation required by the research aim of the program, and the fact that he did not participate in the ordinary rotating system of being on call for emergencies and night visits. The physician's caseload was responsible in part for allowing him to take a good deal of time talking to his patients, but the fact that he was participating in a special preventive program was no doubt also responsible for stimulating him to spend more time "educating" the patients.

However, the physician's relations with patients nonetheless manifested classical authoritative distance. In spite of a rather unusual flexibility in his available time, he still saw his patients largely by appointment—though this is not to say that he would not see someone who happened to drop in when he had a free moment. If he passed through the waiting-room on the way to his office, he did often stop to chat briefly with waiting patients. Nevertheless, unlike the other members of the staff, he stayed in his office to receive patients, sometimes coming to the doorway but rarely stepping through the door out into the waiting-room to greet them. Compared to the other members of the Demonstration staff, his generally briefer time in the office was spent in a far more directly instrumental fashion, though compared to physicians with a "normal" Montefiore Medical Group caseload, he did indeed spend more time in conversation with patients.

From interviews with patients there was extensive evidence of appreciation for being able to talk more freely with the physician and no evidence at all that the physician's authority was lessened either by his willingness to listen to the patients or by his par-

[1] There were two physicians—an internist and a pediatrician. The third person singular is used to express a single role common to both physicians and is intended to describe the observed behavior of both.

ticipation in a "team." Almost every patient interviewed, irrespective of social class, expressed reluctance to "bother" the
physician about minor matters. Indeed, the patients were the
most valuable supporters of the physician's authority, for while
the scope of his authority was frequently limited by other members of the team during the observed *staff* conferences, in conferences in which *both* patients and staff participated the patients
insisted, regardless of the subject matter, on directing their questions to him. Their insistence put him in the position of chief
authority and moderator.

### The Public Health Nurse and the Social Worker

What is unusual about team practice is not the physician but
the other professionals who practiced with him. Most patients
agreed on the importance of the physician in a variety of contexts and utilized his services more than those of any other
workers, but fewer agreed on the importance of the nurse or
social worker. The patients' evaluation of the social worker and
the nurse in everyday health care was the central problem for
the Demonstration.

The title "nurse" has a traditional connotation that is, of
course, medical, and more particularly implies the subordinate
who carries out the doctor's orders. It is hard to guess what
image is conveyed by the title "public health nurse," but on the
whole one cannot believe that it any more than "nurse" is likely
to lead an urban patient to select its bearer as the one most
appropriate source of aid for medical, social, or personal problems. But occupational titles are no solution to our problem here,
because in daily Demonstration practice surnames rather than
titles were used almost entirely. Furthermore, the patients were
not allowed to rest content with their prior conceptions of either
of the new professions involved in the team, and various attempts
were made to inform them of the kind of services they might
obtain from each of the relatively unfamiliar professionals.

Indeed, when it began to seem as though the social workers
were not being utilized properly, a special attempt was made to
"educate" the patients about the social worker's role in the hope

that they might utilize her more extensively. It was not successful, however; most of the patients interviewed remained quite vague about her function. Several thought she dealt "with welfare and problems in the home," or that she was an "investigator . . . the one who . . . investigates social problems and things like that." Some thought she was at the Demonstration to take care of the children while the parents were consulting the doctor, and others could not even guess her function. Similarly, for the nurse, a variety of ideas about her role was revealed in the interviews. Many saw the nurse as assistant to the physician, some as the co-ordinator of all the services of the program, and others as someone "who's there for diet and that sort of thing." Thus, there was confusion about the official roles of both nurse and social worker.

However, in some way, as the questionnaire data have indicated, a difference was communicated, for the social worker was only rarely chosen first. And what is more telling, when patients were specifically referred to her (and in this sense learned directly what her function was) the referral was not often followed. While it may be understandable why one may choose the authoritative physician first, and be reluctant to be referred to a perceived subordinate, it is not easy to understand why one chooses a public health nurse first for a personal problem and is reluctant to be referred to someone who is on much the same status level. Many patients seemed to use the nurse in the way that the social worker was supposed to be used. One said, "Whenever I have problems, I go over to talk to" the nurse. Many mentioned calling her when they had trouble with their children's sleeping and eating habits. One excluded the social worker entirely by making the distinction that the nurse "is more for mental and the doctor is for your physical being." Neither the misunderstandings or emotional resistances of the patients nor the personal characteristics of the professionals themselves seem to be sufficient explanation of the nurse's abrogation of the social worker's role. Rather, it seems necessary to examine the different positions of the nurse and the social worker in the organization of services, and the relationship of those positions to the organized way in which the patients seek help.

## The Nurse

Both the nurse and the social worker were more accessible for informal chats than was the physician. Theoretically, the Demonstration was organized to make both workers equally accessible. But it was the nurse's role that attracted patients. The nurse's initially perceived competence was embedded in the homely problems of everyday life. When the family was enrolled in the program the nurse visited the home to examine sleeping facilities, crowding, diet, and the like. Part of her work was to deal with the problems of housewifery and the objects of domestic consumption. These are the technical subjects, of neutral affect, that form the ground of so much initial interaction between women, no matter how varied their backgrounds. Two wives describe aspects of the work of the nurse below.

> She's been a lot of help with me about diet and about shopping and making out a budget. When my husband was away for a while she knew I had to do all these things and she was wonderful in helping me.

> She helped me bathe the baby. She tried to help me in every possible way. I mean, she takes a very big interest in the family itself. She comes up here to see how we live and how everything is done and the diets and a million and one things.

From initial interaction that establishes communality and, in some cases material usefulness, emerges the probing interplay of conversation that discovers further common interests and points of view, the prerequisite for a less impersonal relationship.

Perhaps more important is the fact that the initial association of the nurse with neutral techniques of domestic efficiency was not of a psychologically threatening character. She was not ostensibly concerned with interpersonal problems that are invested with profound emotions. But it is natural, conversation-wise, to move from housewifery to child-rearing techniques, from there to child problems, and from there to personal problems. Her work may thus easily move toward counseling.

However, this was not the only feature of the nurse's role. Above all, she was a medical worker. She "helps the doctor," and while she was hardly considered to be as authoritative as he about medical matters she was supposed to know enough about medicine to determine whether someone was "really" sick. She could make tentative diagnoses of dimly perceived problems so as to either discourage attention to the problem or to suggest that it might be well to see the physician, as these women believed:

> It was so nice to have someone who could come out to see us and who'd know enough about those things to be able to tell whether we should see the doctor. I think it would be a good idea in HIP to have someone who could visit the home as she did, and who could see people who may really be dying and not know it. And not going to the doctor—they may think they just have a cold or something.

> I usually saw the nurse. Most of my problems were centered around relatively minor illnesses; for example, if Billy had a little infection and I didn't want to bother the doctor about it because I knew it wasn't serious (there was no temperature), I would call the nurse. And she'd tell me what to do and would suggest that if anything developed, if there was a temperature, I call the doctor.

In addition, she was the authoritative source of information about how to treat minor ailments like poison ivy, car-sickness, or "athlete's foot."

The fact that her services were concrete, pervaded everyday life, and were easily accessible, seemed to encourage the use of the nurse on more occasions than were officially appropriate. In the interviews one finds comments that indicate the wide variety of matters taken to her. Several patients who felt slighted by a consulting specialist or by some other physician, mentioned in passing that they had spoken to the nurse about the incident. Many patients considered the nurse to be the administrator of the entire program and others, more modestly, considered her the liaison between them and the doctor in particular and all other professional workers in general.

## The Social Worker

The role of the public health nurse embraced a wide range of activities and preoccupations in concrete and familiar terms.

In contrast, the role of the social worker was supposed to embrace the whole range of daily activities and preoccupations but did so in neither a concrete nor a commonsense fashion. This led to functional specialization of her role that placed her above and beyond the practice of both physician and nurse.

The fundamental isolation of the social worker from everyday consultation was indicated by her role being virtually of an office nature and completely nonmedical. Several patients who perceived behavior problems in their children chose to discuss them with the nurse because they knew it was the nurse who visited their homes and the children's school.[1] They reasoned that the nurse was the one who knew enough about their environment to be able to judge with accuracy its role in their problems. One patient, burdened with shame and frustration by the poor living quarters of his family, complained bitterly that the social worker could not understand his feelings so long as she did not come to see his home. The patients emphasized environmental rather than merely perceptual factors, and what is more, assumed that the field observations of the nurse were not or would not be communicated to the social worker.

The net result of isolation from both medical affairs and the domestic and community environment was that the social worker came to be seen as a specialist—that is, someone to whom it is necessary to go when ordinary techniques have failed and the problem becomes or remains serious. Most patients seemed to define the social worker as a pleasant woman who, if she has any function at all, is a special person unconnected with the day-to-day course of problems with colds, children who will not eat meat, trying to stay on a diet, finding a lump on the groin, or worrying about the children quarreling all the time. These problems—and they are certainly recognized as problems by the patient—were taken to the family doctor, the pediatrician, and the nurse because of the familiar authority of medicine.

[1] It was apparently an administrative decision that the nurse rather than the social worker should have the task of visiting the schools attended by Demonstration children. This makes somewhat puzzling the finding that the social worker is clearly ranked first only for "school problems," unless we assume that the patients were responding on the basis of what they knew about social workers outside the Demonstration.

One woman who had feeding and sleeping problems with her children concerning which she had consulted the nurse said, when asked if she had ever consulted her social worker, "Oh, no, I don't have any problems that need a psychologist or a sociologist." To take these problems to a special person, whether a surgeon or a pleasant woman called a social worker, defines them to be, if not serious, at least no longer normal and everyday. The response of one or two of the patients who told of referrals to the social worker but who had not fully accepted her services sounded a bit like what one might expect from someone who has, to the best of his knowledge, a common cold, like the colds all his friends have from time to time, but who has been strapped to a table and wheeled into an operating room. One patient said that the word "psychiatric" connected with "social worker" occasioned the feeling in him that "all hope is lost and one is pretty much beyond the pale."[1] He had no difficulty accepting his family doctor's services as a counselor.

The patients of the Family Health Maintenance Demonstration did not hesitate to consider their problems to be problems, nor did they on the whole hesitate to bring them to the doctor or the nurse. They were reluctant only to consider their problems to be the sort that required consultation with a special person, for consultation with a special person implied to them that they had passed the bounds of normality. The role of the social worker in the Demonstration made her such a special person.

### The Career of Seeking Help

In the hypothesis that the social worker was not utilized because her role was functionally that of a specialist, there is a set of implicit assumptions that needs further exposition. The most important single assumption is of a patient culture that contains not only norms about the problems patients perceive but also norms about the chronological order of services to seek in getting

[1] For delineations of popular thinking about mental illness see Cumming, John, and Elaine Cumming, "Mental Health Education in a Canadian Community" in *Health, Culture, and Community*, edited by Benjamin F. Paul, Russell Sage Foundation, New York, 1955, pp. 44–69; and Star, Shirley A., "The Place of Psychiatry in Popular Thinking," paper read at the Annual Meeting of the American Association for Public Opinion Research, Washington, 1957.

help for those problems; not only tentative specification of cause and cure but also (given the cause) of the people who, if consulted, are likely to be able to cure.[1] These norms are used to define problems that are solved almost immediately as well as those that more persistently defy solution. In each case, but more particularly in the latter, we must assume a career, a definitely organized course of events in which chronological priority is assigned both to diagnoses of problems and to the procedures and consultants who might cure those problems.

To provide a context for this assumption we must remember that the Demonstration patients are by and large "normal." As normal people they are patients only occasionally—on the average three or four times a year. As normal people, few of whom have had any known contact with hospitals, family courts, and social agencies, they do not have behind them the long series of failures at cure that chronic illness or desperation implies. Therefore, when they do have a problem as patients in the Demonstration, they are in the early stages of a potentially long but probably short career of seeking help. And in the early stages they are likely to explore the least specialized sources of consultation and aid.

In our culture the most ubiquitous diagnostic norm leading to professional consultation refers to states of the physical organism, and the most familiar source of professional consultation is the physician. After "waiting-to-see" there is self-dosing or similar self-treatment, and when those fail there is the doctor. In the same sense, when there are problems with the children that cannot be explained by reference to a "stage that will pass," one tries rest or vitamins and consults a doctor to check the possibility of some physical deficiency as may be found in eyesight, hearing, posture, or nutrition.

---

[1] "Severe illness is always a psychological crisis for the individual and a social crisis for his family. All cultures anticipate such contingencies by furnishing criteria for weighing the severity of the crisis and specifying the steps to be taken when an event is identified as a crisis. Whether or not to call in a specialist, which type of specialist to summon, how to behave in his presence, how to utilize his advice, all depend on how the illness is classified. The category itself is determined as much by cultural definition as by the intrinsic nature of the ailment." Paul, Benjamin F., editor, *op. cit.*, p. 6.

There is also presumed a hierarchy of consultants. Just as one first tries the most commonplace and informal diagnoses of a problem, and only after failure moves to more esoteric diagnoses, so the consultants to whom the norms point vary from the initial use of the commonplace and informal to, after failure of the earlier, the authoritative and formal. They vary from seeking the advice of relatives and friends, for example, to seeking the services of a "big specialist downtown."

### Class Differences in Perceiving Services

With the idea of a career of seeking help in mind, we may reexamine the utilization of Demonstration services. We may note that the nurse is lower than the physician in the hierarchy of authority and formality. If our assumptions are correct we should expect the nurse to be used more rather than less than the physician. Utilization records cannot test that expectation because they proved to provide unreliable evidence about informal consultation. The patients as a whole believed, as we saw, that they used the doctor *more* than the nurse. To explain this contradiction of our expectations, we must examine variations in the patients' social and cultural characteristics.

The nurse's activities revolve around aiding the patient in what might be called his domestic management—sleeping arrangements, diet, budgeting, recreation, and the like—and contributing to his health education—first aid treatment for minor ailments, symptoms requiring consultation with the physician, infant care, and the like. Domestic management is far more of a problem when money is relatively scarce and thus living space, food, and vacations relatively limited. And both domestic management and health education are likely to be important for those with little formal education. The nurse, then, would seem more useful to poorly educated patients than to better-educated, better-off patients. To the former she not only has higher relative status, but also has more to "give."

In the interviews a few of the upper-middle class patients said that they felt little need of the nurse's services—one saying that the nurse was probably "important for poor families" though not for her, and another stressing her own good fortune of having a family of "four in six rooms." The higher the social class, the stronger seemed the patient's feeling that the nurse had not much to offer by way of useful advice. Upper-middle class patients seemed to use the nurse more for her administrative convenience than for her professional knowledge—calling her to get stopgap corroboration of a first-aid measure or to establish contact with the physician. For the upper-middle class patient the public health nurse did not sustain much professional authority either, and so she was bypassed for the physician who had such authority. In turn, the lower the social class the stronger seemed the feeling that the nurse was a kind of substitute doctor—someone who knows enough medicine to be more authoritative than friends and relatives, but who is easier to get hold of and to talk to than the doctor.[1] Lower class patients seemed to use the nurse not only for her administrative services but also extensively for her advice.

Differences in class culture are also reflected in views of the social worker. The sharpest contrast is between the lower class of semi-skilled workers and the upper-middle class of professional workers. The lower class patients who were interviewed, like those studied by others, were far less prone than the upper-middle class patients to perceive their problems in psychological terms. They saw their problems as having physical or environmental causes. If their problems were believed to be caused by an individual's behavior, lower class patients were inclined to explain the behavior as a fundamentally immutable aspect of personal character rather than something that could be manipulated or changed by insight or counseling. Insofar as they actually understood what the social worker was for, lower class patients would thus be likely to avoid her and to utilize instead the nurse and the physician. What use they would make of the social worker would tend to be restricted to problems that they saw as

---

[1] On the nurse and class differences see: Wellin, Edward, "Water Boiling in a Peruvian Town" in Paul, Benjamin F., *op. cit.*, pp. 71–103; Simmons, Ozzie G., "The Clinical Team in a Chilean Health Center," *ibid.*, pp. 325–348; and especially Simmons, Ozzie G., *Social Status and Public Health*, Pamphlet no. 13, Social Science Research Council, New York, 1958.

environmental in character—aid for an indigent relative, aid in getting into a low-income housing project, and the like.

Upper-middle class patients, in contrast, were relatively more up-to-date, almost as prone to diagnose their problems in psychological as in physical or environmental terms. What is more, they seemed considerably more insecure in the knowledge they felt they had about psychological problems than in the knowledge they felt they had about medical or housekeeping problems. Along with their more accurate knowledge of the function of the modern social worker, their relatively clearer perception of need for counseling should lead us to expect that upper-middle class patients be somewhat more positively oriented to the social worker than lower class patients, more likely to use her for aid in psychological than in environmental problems.

In essence, it has been suggested not that utilization would vary by social class so much as that particular kinds of utilization would vary. The available records of the Demonstration do not distinguish between use for counseling and for help with environmental problems; therefore, we have no objective source of quantitative data by which we may test these suggestions. All that we have available is evidence of the patients' *conceptions* of utilization—the choices they made in two questionnaires. This evidence, such as it is, provides consistent corroboration of the class differences suggested by the interviews. When asked to consider a hypothetical situation in which the Family Health Maintenance Demonstration had to dispense with the services of either the social worker or the public health nurse, the proportion of upper-middle class patients choosing to retain the social worker was greater than that of lower class; choice to retain the public health nurse was more frequent by lower class patients than by upper-middle class. This is indicated in Table 4.

Additional evidence is provided by tabulating by social class the staff rankings that the patients made in response to questions about utilization, its context, and hypothetical problems on the basis of which utilization might take place. (See Tables 2 and 3.) These tabulations were remarkably consistent in spite of the variety of questions. While differences were small in some cases, the

TABLE 4. CHOICE BETWEEN STAFF WORKERS[a], BY WARNER
OCCUPATIONAL SCALE[b]

| "If it were necessary to choose between having the services of a public health nurse . . . and the services of a social worker . . . how would you choose? Make your choice on the basis of your own needs and past experience." | Highest occupational groups (1 and 2) | (3 and 4) | Lowest occupational groups (5, 6, 7) |
|---|---|---|---|
| | | *Per cent* | |
| If I couldn't have both, would prefer having a social worker | 32 | 26 | 17 |
| If I couldn't have both, would prefer having a public health nurse | 54 | 62 | 67 |
| Makes no difference which one | 14 | 12 | 16 |
| N | (69) | (74) | (81) |

$X^2 = 4.72$, $p < .70$. Tabulating columns 1 and 3 against rows 1 and 2, $X^2 = 3.87$, $p < .05$.

 [a] In a questionnaire administered two years later, after the Demonstration had concluded, answers to the same question were of the same pattern, somewhat more marked.

 [b] The Warner rankings are to be found in Warner, W. Lloyd, Marcia Meeker, and Kenneth Eells, *Social Class in America*. Science Research Associates, Chicago, 1949.

*direction* of difference was in no case contradictory. In answering the questions in *no* instance did a greater proportion of upper-middle than lower class patients choose the nurse; in *no* instances did a greater proportion of lower than upper-middle class patients choose the social worker. While the nurse was more often chosen than the social worker by *all* patients regardless of social class, *more* of the lower class chose her in preference to the social worker for assistance in each of a variety of problems. While the social worker was less often chosen than the nurse by *all* patients regardless of class, *more* of the upper-middle class chose her in preference to the nurse.

## The Structure of Staff-Patient Interaction

To summarize: the nurse was successfully introduced into everyday health practice because (1) her services were compatible with prevailing client conceptions of the nature of their problems, and (2) her services were relatively informal and highly accessible. Consequently, her services could be used during the early stage of the career of seeking help—a stage to be expected of "normal" people in a preventive program which attempts to teach them that they have *immanent* problems. Use of her services, or of the somewhat more authoritarian but nonetheless everyday, familiar services of the physician, is likely to continue until the problem comes to be perceived as serious or at least special and not amenable to everyday treatment. When the problem reaches that point, the social worker is more likely to be accepted.

The social worker was less successfully introduced into everyday team practice. Her services were underutilized because of their incompatibility with prevailing patient conceptions of the nature of the problems needing professional help. This isolated them as specialized services for serious problems. Unsuccessful referral of the patient to the social worker by other members of the program seemed to result from her functional position as a relatively late source of consultation for "special" problems: the patients were too "normal"; that is, they were involved at a very early point in the process of perceiving a problem and exploring familiar consultants, and had not developed sufficient sense of failure to take the next step toward less familiar consultants.

Analysis was predicated on the fact that patients have norms about illness that differ from professional norms and that patient norms are used in an ordered process of seeking "cure." This process very often involves the successive use of more than one norm in defining an illness, a certain order of priority guiding the choice of the norm likely to be used first. It also involves an ordering of norms that designate who is "appropriately" consulted at each stage of the problem. The ordering of steps in the process of seeking that help constitutes a structure that sustains patient culture. This structure allows us to see how two people with the same problem but in different stages of their careers of seeking help can have different relationships with a single professional consultant. The content of the structure allows us to see something of the way a prospective consultant may "fit in" and be used only at particular points of the career.

Naturally, norms vary from group to group. In the course of suggesting that the upper-middle class patients had norms about their problems that differed from those of lower class patients, there was occasion to make more detailed examination of patient responses to the staff of the Demonstration. The available evidence suggests that upper-middle class patients were more likely than lower class to use the social worker for counseling and to look favorably upon her services. The upper-middle class patient is less likely to have to be desperate or far advanced in his experience of seeking help before he will consider using her.

The critical point introduced in this chapter is that choice and utilization of professional services may be understood as a function of the relation of the content and the organization of those professional services to the content and organization of the process by which the patient seeks help. In the following chapters more attention will be paid the interaction between professional and lay social systems as we examine a more definite problem of utilization—occasions in which patients chose to use an entrepreneurial practitioner's services rather than those of the Montefiore Medical Group and the Family Health Maintenance Demonstration.

# 6. Choices Between Medical Practices[1]

In DISCUSSING THE USE OF SERVICES of the various personnel of the Family Health Maintenance Demonstration, it became apparent that patient satisfaction did not mean that all facets of the program were accepted with open arms. Satisfaction hinged on having access to what was desirable about the program and at the same time on being allowed to put up with passively, or to ignore or bypass what was not desirable. The qualified character of patient satisfaction is most easily seen in instances where patients chose to use the services of entrepreneurial physicians rather than those of the Family Health Maintenance Demonstration or the Montefiore Medical Group.

## The Use of Outside Physicians

Let us recall that 100 per cent of the adult patients of the Demonstration who responded said that "on the whole [they] liked being a member of the Demonstration." Ninety-eight per cent expressed satisfaction with the medical care of the Demonstration. Eighty-four per cent felt that they received better medical care from the Demonstration than from their prior entrepreneurial physician, and 14 per cent felt Demonstration care was at least as good. In view of their enthusiasm, it is startling that when they were asked,[2] "While you've been in

[1] Portions of this chapter have already been reported in Freidson, Eliot, "The Organization of Medical Practice and Patient Behavior," *American Journal of Public Health*, vol. 51, January, 1961, pp. 43–52. Reprinted by permission of the American Public Health Association.

[2] In answering the following questions the patients were asked to "ignore the occasions when you were out of town and could not get HIP care."

Family Health, did you or any eligible member of your family have a surgical operation (or child delivery) performed by a private doctor?" 15 per cent of the families (using the wife's response in each instance to represent the family's) answered, "Yes." Eleven of that 15 per cent paid for the operation out of their own pockets. Asked, "Excluding operations now, while you've been in Family Health, did you or any eligible member of your family use the services of a private doctor?" 6 per cent of the families answered, "Yes, quite a bit," and 31 per cent of the families answered, "Yes, occasionally." The Family Health Maintenance Demonstration patients were also asked, "Before you were in Family Health and when you were a regular HIP subscriber, did you or any member of your family eligible for HIP care ever have a surgical operation (or child delivery) performed by a private medical doctor?" Twenty-one per cent of those responding[1] answered, "Yes, at our own expense," and an additional 2 per cent answered, "Yes, on Blue Shield, to which we also belong." Asked further, "Excluding operations now, before you were in Family Health, while you were a regular HIP subscriber, did you or any member of your family eligible for HIP care use the services of a private doctor?" Of those responding, 16 per cent answered, "Yes, quite a bit," and 29 per cent answered, "Yes, occasionally."

It is clear that this behavior existed before entering the Family Health Maintenance Demonstration and persisted during participation in the program. Indeed, in a followup questionnaire administered one year after all subscribers had finally been discharged from the program and had become regular Montefiore Medical Group patients again, 5 per cent reported the use of an outside physician or surgeon for a surgical operation or a child delivery since leaving the Demonstration. Forty-two per cent indicated the use of outside physicians for nonsurgical and nonobstetrical services since leaving the Demonstration.

Table 5 presents the data in a way that allows comparison of all reports of outside utilization, including those of the regular

---

[1] In this and the following instances, 25 families who returned the questionnaires did not respond largely because they were subscribers for only a few months before entering the Family Health Maintenance Demonstration.

Medical Group subscribers who, like the Demonstration patients, were covered by a family rather than by an individual insurance contract. The period of enrollment in the plan is, as we shall see later, an important correlate of reported outside use, but the number of Demonstration families was too small to allow more than mere indication of the time periods involved. A warning: The percentages for the use of surgical-obstetrical services may *not* be added to those for the use of nonsurgical, nonobstetrical services, since the same family could and often did report both types of utilization.

TABLE 5. REPORTED USE OF OUTSIDE PHYSICIANS BY MONTEFIORE MEDICAL GROUP AND FAMILY HEALTH MAINTENANCE DEMONSTRATION PATIENTS

| Type of outside service used | Montefiore Medical Group family contract subscribers[b] (N = 307) | Family Health Maintenance Demonstration families | | |
| --- | --- | --- | --- | --- |
| | | In HIP before FHMD[c] (N = 93) | During FHMD[d] (N = 117) | In HIP after FHMD[e] (N = 85) |
| | | *Per cent*[f] | | |
| Surgical-obstetrical services[a] | 17 | 23 | 15 | 5 |
| Nonsurgical, nonobstetrical services | 48 | 45 | 37 | 42 |

[a] Instances where HIP paid the cost of such outside services (and thereby acknowledged the legitimacy of their use) are excluded.

[b] Sixty-four per cent had been subscribers for more than four years.

[c] At the time of entering the Demonstration, patients had been enrolled in the Montefiore Medical Group for an average of two and a half years.

[d] At the time of the questionnaire the respondents had been in the Family Health Maintenance Demonstration for an average of three years.

[e] The responding patients had been discharged from the Family Health Maintenance Demonstration for an average of somewhat less than two years.

[f] As noted in the text, these percentages may *not* be added.

It might be argued that Table 5 shows that the level of reported outside utilization of nonsurgical, nonobstetrical services dropped significantly when patients received Family Health Maintenance Demonstration care. That the level did drop is indubitable; and it rose somewhat upon the patient's return to Medical Group care. However, the significance of the data is problematic. The table is presented primarily to show that the use of outside services is a widespread phenomenon among the subscribers whether or not they have been patients of the Family Health Maintenance Demonstration.[1]

## The Background

In our surveys of the use of outside physicians, the necessity for administering questionnaires by mail required brevity and simplicity. For this reason little effort was made to determine anything more than the mere existence of outside utilization. However, one important distinction was made in the Montefiore Medical Group survey—the use of an outside doctor "for most medical needs, hardly using HIP at all," and the use of an outside doctor for some services but the continued use of HIP "for most medical needs." In the first case we have regular use of an outside physician, while in the second we have only occasional use. However, it must be remembered that we lack any information about the absolute number of times in which outside services are used. In regular use of outside medical services we may reasonably assume that the prepaid practice is being used little. But for occasional use of outside services, by the very nature of the question asked—"Did you *ever* use the service of a non-HIP doctor?"—the answer, "Yes, have used a non-HIP doctor, but HIP has been used for most medical needs," could be made when use took place only once during the entire enrollment and also when use took place several times a year. Occasional use of outside services is likely to be less sustained and more casual than regular use of such services, but exactly how casual cannot be determined from the questionnaire responses.

---

[1] All such formal plans as HIP seem to experience outside utilization of medical services on the part of subscribers. In a citywide sample of HIP subscribers, 33 per cent of all operations during 1951 were reported to have been performed by outside physicians. (See Committee for the Special Research Project in the Health Insurance Plan of Greater New York, *Health and Medical Care in New York City*, Harvard University Press, Cambridge, Mass., 1957, p. 169.) On another HIP group, see Rothenberg, Robert E., Karl Pickard, and Joel E. Rothenberg, *Group Medicine and Health Insurance in Action*, Crown Publishers, New York, 1949, pp. 215–216. A study of patients of the Labor Health Institute found that 48 per cent of the sample reported outside medical and dental care during the year prior to study, 70.5 per cent of those outside services having been rendered by a physician. See Simon, Nathan, and Sanford Rubushka, "Membership Attitudes in the Labor Health Institute of St. Louis," *American Journal of Public Health*, vol. 46, June, 1956, pp. 716–722.

In the survey of Montefiore Medical Group patients only subscribers were questioned, not all the adult members of subscribing families. It covered a greater variety of family and contract situations than was present in the Family Health Maintenance Demonstration. The exact degree of this variety is evident in the following characteristics of the subscribers: 61 per cent were males and 39 per cent females; 41 per cent were in the child-bearing and child-rearing ages below forty-five, 42 per cent between forty-five and sixty, and 17 per cent sixty and over. Seventy-nine per cent were married, 3 per cent divorced or separated, 8 per cent widowed and 10 per cent never married, but only 45 per cent had a "family contract" for medical care that included the spouse and children under eighteen. Twenty-seven per cent had two-person contracts and 28 per cent had a contract that covered care only for themselves. Sixty-four per cent of the respondents had been subscribers for more than four years.

Somewhat more than half of the subscribers (57 per cent) reported that they themselves had had at some time in their lives "a surgical operation (or child delivery) requiring hospitalization," but less than half—43 per cent—reported that either they or some member of their families had had such a procedure performed by a HIP doctor. That this is largely a function of the short time HIP has existed and the short period they had been HIP subscribers is indicated by the fact that of those who had been subscribers for two years or less, only 17 per cent reported such an operation or child delivery performed by a HIP doctor, compared to 31 per cent of those who had been subscribers between two and four years and 53 per cent for more than four years.

The Montefiore Medical Group subscribers did not report very heavy use of medical services. Asked, "During the past two years, how many times have you yourself had to see a doctor?" 8 per cent indicated they had not seen a doctor at all, 48 per cent indicated their use to have been once or twice a year, 22 per cent indicated seeing a doctor three or four times a year, and an additional 22 per cent reported their use to be five times a year or more. Almost identical proportions were reported by married subscribers of use by their spouses, though there is a tendency for subscribers with children to report that their children see a doctor more often than they do.

As we noted in Chapter 3, a very large proportion of the subscribers express positive attitudes toward the Medical Group, its physicians, and its care. But when asked, "Since you've been in HIP have you or any member of your family covered by HIP had an operation (or a baby delivered) by a non-HIP doctor?" 12 per cent of the 604 responding answered, "Yes, at our own expense." An additional 3 per cent answered, "Yes, expenses paid by Blue Shield or some other surgical plan to which we also belong," and another 3 per cent answered, "Yes, but HIP paid our expenses." Of these instances of "outside surgery" reported, 75 per cent involved the wife of the family, a finding enforced by the report that 41 per cent of all "surgical" outside use involved childbirth and an additional 26 per cent involved feminine operative procedures like dilettage and curetage, hysterectomy and mastectomy. Sixty-one per cent of the instances reported involved the use of a physician who was known by the subscriber before he had joined HIP.

The sample of subscribers to the Montefiore Medical Group was also asked, "Except for operations, during the time you have been in HIP, did you or any member of your family covered by HIP use the services of a non-HIP doctor?" Ten per cent of 635 answered, "Yes, use a non-HIP doctor for most medical needs, hardly using HIP at all." Another 36 per cent answered, "Yes, have used a non-HIP doctor, but HIP has been used for most medical needs." The remaining 54 per cent answered, "No, never used non-HIP doctors while entitled to HIP care." Of these instances of outside utilization reported, 60 per cent involved the wife of the family, 46 per cent the husband, and 48 per cent the children.[1] Significantly, those reporting *regular* outside use tended to report more members of the family involved than did those reporting occasional outside utilization—the

[1] Some respondents reported more than one member of the family using outside services; hence, the percentages add up to more than 100.

former reported an average of 2.01 different members of the family involved compared to 1.41 reported by the latter.

### The Use of Outside Surgical-Obstetrical Services

Now that we have some idea of the way in which the sample of subscribers responded as a whole, we can explore the variables associated with their reported behavior. In doing so, we will deal only briefly with reported use of outside surgical-obstetrical services, primarily because there are too few instances to allow more than the simplest tabulations.

Some cases of outside utilization of surgical-obstetrical services may be understood solely by reference to technical, administrative problems. For example, the 3 per cent who indicated that they were reimbursed by HIP for their "outside" operation or delivery do not interest us very much, for their behavior was seen by the contracting agency to be justified, whether because of being out of the area of coverage, or an emergency, or the like. Similarly, we are not particularly interested in an additional 3 per cent who indicated that they were reimbursed by another insurance plan when they went "outside" HIP, for insofar as their choice to go outside did not involve deliberate acceptance of the penalty of out-of-pocket expense, it is hard to consider it to have been a critical choice. These two groups, comprising 6 per cent of the respondents, were therefore eliminated from further tabulations. An additional 2 per cent were also eliminated because, while they did use outside surgical-obstetrical care and paid for this out of pocket, the reasons they gave for their behavior involved either a sudden emergency when there was no time for deliberate choice or contract coverage that did not allow use of HIP facilities.[1] The remaining instances of reported use of outside surgical-obstetrical services represent cases where outside use is most likely to have been motivated by strong feelings and critical experiences.

What are the characteristics of those who chose outside surgical-obstetrical services that distinguish them from those who

[1] Most commonly cited as a problem of coverage was surgery for cosmetic purposes.

did not so choose? There was no important sex difference, but subscribers most often reporting outside utilization were those in the child-rearing period between twenty-nine and forty-five years of age. They were married, had a contract covering their spouses and children, and had children young enough to use a pediatrician. Thus, the type of subscriber chosen for the Family Health Maintenance Demonstration was most likely to use outside services in the first place. A large proportion were long-term subscribers, having been enrolled in HIP for more than four years, and they tended to be of higher occupational and educational attainment than those who had not used outside services.

Their attitudes toward HIP and the Montefiore Medical Group were more critical and negative. They were less likely to feel that HIP doctors were better than the doctors they had before joining the plan, less likely to think they received better medical care from the Montefiore Medical Group than from doctors before joining HIP and considerably more likely to feel that the doctors they had previously were more interested in them than HIP doctors. In addition, they were more likely to feel that their HIP pediatricians and the HIP specialists did not take as much interest in them as they should. While few complained of lack of interest on the part of the Family Doctors, a comparatively large proportion did indicate that at one time or another they had asked to change their Family Doctor. A comparatively large proportion felt that the Montefiore Medical Group had a "clinic atmosphere," and more indicated general dissatisfaction with the care they had received at the Medical Group than was true of patients who reported no utilization of outside surgical-obstetrical services.

## The Use of Outside Medical Services

Sixty-eight per cent of those who reported the use of outside surgical-obstetrical services also reported the use of outside medical services.[1] Thus, while surgery and child delivery are hardly

[1] For convenience, the term "medical" will sometimes be used to indicate non-surgical, nonobstetrical services.

commonplace events, and hardly constitute topics of continuous, day-to-day preoccupation, the tendency to go outside to obtain them is closely associated with the use of more everyday outside services. Since only 63 cases of outside surgery were involved in our survey, nothing much could be done with them by way of exploratory cross-tabulations, but given the association it seems reasonable to assume that at least some of the parameters significant to such outside utilization are also significant to the utilization of outside physicians for nonsurgical care. In the utilization of outside nonsurgical, nonobstetrical services there is a sufficient number of cases to allow some, though still not all, apparently important variables to be examined. Furthermore, we are able to deal with two quite different patterns of outside utilization simply by the distinction between regular and occasional use.

There are three types of utilization. They allow us to distinguish three types of patients: (1) Patients who may be called "regular outside users" are the subscribers who indicated that they "use a non-HIP doctor for most medical needs, hardly using HIP at all." Here we may assume *avoidance* of the Montefiore Medical Group, and everyday use of outside service. (2) Patients who may be called "occasional outside users" are those who indicated that they have used a non-HIP doctor on one occasion or another, "but HIP has been used for most medical needs." Here we may *not* assume avoidance of the Montefiore Medical Group; we may assume merely that there are particular occasions that encourage outside use and particular patient attributes that allow it. (3) Finally, patients who may be called "nonusers of outside services" are those who indicated that they "never used non-HIP doctors while entitled to HIP care."

Each type of patient is not differentiated from the other by age, marital status, or type of insurance contract. Nor do the types differ in reporting the number of times they or their spouses, if married, have had to consult a doctor over the two years preceding the administration of the questionnaire. However, while about the same proportions of both nonusers (45 per cent) and occasional outside users (47 per cent) reported that they or some member of their family had had an operation or a baby delivered by a HIP doctor, this is reported by considerably fewer—22 per cent—of the regular outside users. And while 38 per cent of the regular users of outside services reported having had outside surgical or obstetrical services when the period of enrollment was controlled, this was the case for only 18 per cent of the occasional users and for 10 per cent of those who used no outside medical services. The regular outside user's behavior is thus more consistently oriented to outside practice than the behavior of the other patients.

A number of factors appear to be important here. One is the sheer time it takes for grievance to be generated among subscribers. Assuming that experiences in the Montefiore Medical Group which might provoke grievance or dissatisfaction are randomly distributed, and assuming that it is only such experience that sends people to outside physicians (rather than the preconceptions which the patient is likely to bring to his experience), we should expect that the longer the patient is enrolled in the Medical Group the more is he likely to have had an experience which moves him to seek outside medical care. We have already noted that this is true for the use of outside surgical or obstetrical services, but we can test the hypothesis better for the use of outside medical services because of the larger number of cases. The hypothesis is tested in Table 6, which shows that the longer the patient is in the Group the more likely is he to have

TABLE 6. PERIOD OF PATIENT ENROLLMENT IN HIP AND USE OF OUTSIDE SERVICES

|  | Two years or less | Between two and four years | More than four years |
|---|---|---|---|
|  | *Per cent* | | |
| Regular use of outside services | 11 | 11 | 10 |
| Occasional use of outside services | 21 | 36 | 41 |
| Never used outside services | 68 | 53 | 49 |
| N | (133) | (81) | (418) |

$X^2 = 18.13$, p < .01

made *occasional* use of an outside physician.[1] But what gives one pause is the fact that this is not true of the *regular* use of outside services, the proportion of which does not change with time.[2]

Since the time to generate grievance does not wholly explain the use of outside services, we may turn to the role of cultural differences. Ethnic background is a common source of cultural difference and seems particularly appropriate to examine as a variable in The Bronx, where there is a relatively large proportion of foreign-born and first-generation patients. With time enrolled in HIP controlled, Table 7 shows that subscribers of Irish background are more often regular users of outside services

TABLE 7. ETHNIC BACKGROUND AND THE USE OF OUTSIDE
MEDICAL SERVICES
(Patients enrolled in HIP for more than four years)

|  |  | Irish | Jewish | Italian |
|---|---|---|---|---|
|  |  | *Per cent* | | |
| Regular use of outside services |  | 15 | 8 | 8 |
| Occasional use of outside services |  | 38 | 50 | 24 |
| Never used outside services |  | 47 | 42 | 68 |
|  | N | (68) | (221) | (49) |

$X^2 = 14.35$, $p < .01$

than we would expect by chance, Jewish subscribers more often occasional users of outside services, and Italian more often non-users of outside services.

Ethnic background, however, is not the only source of cultural difference. In the United States many studies have shown how social class differences include cultural differences. So it seems appropriate to ask what would happen to the association of ethnic background with outside utilization if the variable of social class were controlled. Using education and occupation as a

[1] N. M. Simon and S. E. Rubushka in *A Trade Union and Its Medical Service Plan* (Labor Health Institute, St. Louis, 1954) report that the longer a person is in the group plan they studied, the less is he likely to go outside.

[2] If we were to combine rows one and two—that is, lump all outside utilization together—the hypothesis would appear to have been completely confirmed. So can the neatest array conceal significant exceptions.

measure of social class, Table 8[1] compares the use of services by all patients in the same class, distinguishing the patients by their ethnic backgrounds, and shows that the differences between the Jews and the Irish are negligible, though both differ somewhat from the Italians. The number of cases involved prevents testing statistical significance except by combining both types of outside utilization. When they are combined, differences in utilization are not statistically significant. Ethnic background seems to be a considerably less important variable than social class.

TABLE 8. ETHNIC BACKGROUND AND USE OF OUTSIDE SERVICES, EDUCATION AND OCCUPATION CONTROLLED[a]

|  | | Irish | Jewish | Italian |
|---|---|---|---|---|
|  | | | Per cent | |
| Regular use of outside services | | 20 | 17 | 9 |
| Occasional use of outside services | | 27 | 28 | 18 |
| Never used outside services | | 53 | 55 | 73 |
|  | N | (26) | (29) | (22) |

Combining rows 1 and 2 because of small numbers, $X^2 = 2.49$, $p < .30$

[a] All patients went to high school, no further, and are in rank 5 of Warner's occupational scale.

Indeed, social class is a useful variable because it embraces not only "culture"—that is to say, attitudes and values that may dispose people to respond positively or negatively to a way of organizing medical care—but also economic standing. It is obvious that those who use services outside the Montefiore Medical Group are in a sense paying double fees—they pay a subscription, which entitles them to HIP care, and pay an additional fee for each instance of outside utilization. People with a high income are more likely to be able to afford that additional fee than are those having a low income. Thus, we should expect that while everyone enrolled in the Montefiore Medical Group may at one time or another *wish* to consult an "outside" doctor, those with a higher income are more likely to *do* so. Using education as a measure of social class and, indirectly, income, tabula-

[1] There were too few cases to allow controlling for the period of time the respondents were enrolled in HIP.

tion shows in Table 9 that those of the lower level tend to be nonusers of outside services, those of the higher level tend to be occasional users of outside services. When our percentages are run *across* the table, we may note further that 66 per cent of those who use outside services occasionally have had at least some college education, compared to 44 per cent of those who use no outside services. Using occupational status rather than education as our measure of social class, the same regular pattern is obtained on the same level of significance. This partially confirms our expectations,[1] but regular use of outside medical services again is an exception, tending to be rather evenly distributed throughout the ranks.

TABLE 9. EDUCATION AND USE OF OUTSIDE SERVICES
(Patients enrolled in HIP more than four years)

|  | Graduated from college | Some college training | Graduated from high school | Some high school training | Grammar school education or less |
|---|---|---|---|---|---|
|  | *Per cent* | | | | |
| Regular use of outside services | 8 | 9 | 14 | 11 | 12 |
| Occasional use of outside services | 55 | 45 | 31 | 30 | 25 |
| Never used outside services | 37 | 46 | 55 | 59 | 63 |
| N | (150) | (69) | (73) | (63) | (60) |

$X^2 = 26.29$, $p < .001$

Social class, however, involves more than mere ability to pay. It also involves a subjective component that is associated with one's sense of self and expectation of the way others will treat him. Obviously, what will dissatisfy one person with a doctor may not dissatisfy another, and on the whole we would expect patients of higher standing to be somewhat more sensitive to a

[1] The Committee for the Special Research Project in the Health Insurance Plan of Greater New York (*op. cit.*, p. 85), reports the opposite; that is, the higher the education of a HIP subscriber sample, the lower the amount of outside utilization of medical services. Obviously, much remains to be sifted out here, but it seems far more plausible that outside utilization will vary directly with education. In England income was found to be associated with use of a physician on a "private," non-National Health Service basis. See Gray, P. G., and Ann Cartwright, "General Practice Under the National Health Service," The Social Survey, London, n.d., pp. 5–6; mimeographed.

doctor's manner and to the "setting" of medical services than those of lower standing. Education is, in fact, associated with responses to two questions which attempt to elicit expressions of "status sensitivity." Seventy-eight per cent of those in the highest educational group compared to 90 per cent of those in the lowest reported that they had never been insulted by a doctor; 41 per cent of those in the highest educational group compared to 67 per cent of those in the lowest reported that they failed to perceive a "clinic atmosphere" in the Medical Group.

Considering status sensitivity to be one of the subjective components of social class, we see from Table 10 that more of the

TABLE 10. EXPRESSION OF STATUS SENSITIVITY AND USE OF OUTSIDE SERVICES
(Patients enrolled in HIP more than four years)

| Questions and answers | Regular users of outside services | Occasional users of outside services | Nonusers of outside services | N (100 per cent) |
|---|---|---|---|---|
| "Did you or your wife or husband ever have an experience with a doctor when you felt that you were *insulted*?" | | *Per cent* | | |
| Yes | 18 | 49 | 33 | ( 84) |
| No, never | 8 | 39 | 53 | (326) |
| $X^2 = 14.08$, p < .001 | | | | |
| "Some people say that the Montefiore Group has a clinic atmosphere that makes them feel they are charity cases. Do you agree?" | | | | |
| Yes, very much | 30 | 44 | 26 | ( 61) |
| Yes, a bit | 8 | 48 | 44 | (160) |
| No, not at all | 5 | 34 | 61 | (192) |
| $X^2 = 46.81$, p < .001 | | | | |

people perceiving "insult" and "clinic atmosphere" used outside services than those not so sensitive.[1] This is in accord with our

[1] The same pattern on the same level of significance is yielded by tabulating patients' comparisons of the "personal interest" doctors take in them in entrepreneurial practice and in the Medical Group. This, too, can be interpreted as a measure of "status sensitivity."

expectations for the occasional outside use of services (which is associated with the objective class measures of education and occupation), but not for regular use. The association with sensitivity is strongest of all for the regular use of outside services, but the latter is *not* associated with objective measures of social class. Social class in both its objective and subjective facets, like time enrolled in the plan, thus discriminates between use and nonuse of outside services, but not between the two types of use. Differences in *attitude*, however, prove to distinguish among regular and occasional as well as nonuse of outside services, but since the number of cases is too small to allow determining the importance of each attitude, we must use them only descriptively.

Calculating the percentages down instead of across Table 10, we see that each type of patient is prone to differ in his sensitivity: 36 per cent of the regular outside users reported being insulted by a doctor, compared to 24 per cent of the occasional outside users and 14 per cent of the nonusers; only 22.5 per cent of the regular outside users failed to agree that the Medical Group has a "clinic atmosphere," compared to 38 per cent of the occasional outside users and 58 per cent of the nonusers of outside services.

Furthermore, the regular user of outside services has a marked tendency to believe that entrepreneurial medical services are superior to those of the Medical Group. As we see in Table 11, a very large proportion of them believed that their prior doctors were better doctors and more interested in them than those in the Medical Group, and that they provided better care. The other patients, nonusers more than occasional outside users, were considerably more appreciative of their HIP services.

But while the occasional user of outside services is relatively uncommitted to either method of providing services, he is characteristically critical and active in his approach to medical care, something we might expect from this better-educated group. His critical attitude is shared with the regular user of outside services and the two are rather distinct from the patient who uses none. Indeed, the latter seems rather uncritical in his approach to medical care. As we see in Table 12, the same differences among the patients apply to answers to questions dealing with shopping

## TABLE 11. USE OF OUTSIDE SERVICES AND EVALUATION OF MEDICAL SERVICES

(Patients enrolled in HIP more than four years)

| Questions and answers | Regular users of outside services | Occasional users of outside services | Nonusers of outside services |
|---|---|---|---|
| | *Per cent* | | |
| QUALITY OF DOCTORS: | | | |
| "Does it seem to you that on the whole HIP doctors are *better doctors* than the ones you had before you joined HIP?" | | | |
| Yes, HIP doctors are better | 3 | 3 | 25 |
| HIP and non-HIP doctors are about the same | 42 | 83 | 70 |
| Non-HIP doctors are better | 55 | 14 | 5 |
| $N^a$ | (29) | (146) | (167) |
| $X^2 = 77.21$, $p < .001$ | | | |
| DOCTOR INTEREST: | | | |
| "Does it seem to you that on the whole the doctors in HIP are more interested in you than the doctors you had before you joined HIP?" | | | |
| Yes, HIP doctors are more interested | 3 | 16 | 37 |
| HIP and non-HIP doctors are about the same | 27 | 41 | 44 |
| No, non-HIP doctors are more interested | 70 | 43 | 19 |
| N | (37) | (167) | (198) |
| $X^2 = 56.82$, $p < .001$ | | | |
| QUALITY OF MEDICAL CARE: | | | |
| "Do you think that on the whole you've gotten better medical care from the Montefiore Group than you got from non-HIP doctors before you belonged to HIP?" | | | |
| Yes, got better medical care from Group | 14 | 49 | 59 |
| Medical care from Group and non-HIP doctors was about the same | 32 | 36 | 36 |
| No, got better medical care from non-HIP doctors | 54 | 15 | 5 |
| N | (35) | (155) | (193) |
| $X^2 = 62.94$, $p < .001$ | | | |

ᵃ Variation in the number of respondents stems largely from variation in the number of "Don't knows," which are not tabulated here.

TABLE 12. USE OF OUTSIDE SERVICES AND CRITICAL RESPONSE TO MEDICAL SERVICES

(Patients enrolled in HIP more than four years)

| Questions and answers | Regular users of outside services | Occasional users of outside services | Nonusers of outside services |
|---|---|---|---|
| | *Per cent* | | |
| "Shopping around": | | | |
| "Have you or your wife or husband ever gone to a second doctor to get his opinion about some condition *without telling your first doctor* about going?" | | | |
| Yes, before I belonged to HIP | 2.5 | 8 | 13 |
| Yes, when I belonged to HIP | 36 | 28 | 3.5 |
| Yes, several times before and while I belonged to HIP | 20.5 | 17 | 3.5 |
| No, never                 N[a] | 41 (39) | 47 (167) | 80 (202) |
| $X^2 = 85.96$, p<.001 | | | |
| Dissatisfaction: | | | |
| "Have you or your wife or husband ever stopped going to a doctor because you weren't satisfied with him?" | | | |
| Yes, a non-HIP doctor only | 18 | 17 | 24 |
| Yes, a HIP doctor only | 31 | 14 | 7 |
| Yes, both a non-HIP and a HIP doctor | 20 | 25 | 11 |
| No, never                 N | 31 (39) | 44 (167) | 58 (201) |
| $X^2 = 34.26$, p<.001 | | | |
| Imputing incompetence: | | | |
| "Did you or your wife or husband ever have a doctor who seemed to be incompetent?" | | | |
| Yes, a non-HIP doctor only | 7.5 | 9 | 14 |
| Yes, a HIP doctor only | 25 | 15 | 6.5 |
| Yes, both HIP and non-HIP doctors | 10 | 15 | 8 |
| No, never                 N | 57.5 (40) | 61 (170) | 71.5 (197) |
| $X^2 = 20.68$, p<.01 | | | |

[a] Variation in the number of respondents is due to occasional failure to answer the question.

around for medical opinions, "dropping" a doctor because of dissatisfaction with him, and judging a doctor to be incompetent.[1]

While both regular and occasional users of outside services prove to be rather critical in their attitudes, however, the patient who regularly uses outside physicians tends to be considerably more passive in his response to the Medical Group than the patient who only occasionally uses outside services. Subscribers to HIP have the right to ask for a different physician if they are dissatisfied with their Family Doctor. The patients were asked if

TABLE 13. USE OF OUTSIDE SERVICES AND REQUEST FOR CHANGE OF DOCTOR

(Patients enrolled in HIP more than four years)

| "Have you ever asked to change your HIP Family Doctor?" | Regular users of outside services | Occasional users of outside services | Nonusers of outside services |
|---|---|---|---|
| | *Per cent* | | |
| Yes, I've asked to change my doctor | 23 | 36 | 18 |
| No, but I've sometimes wanted to change | 33 | 23 | 18 |
| No, and I never wanted to change | 44 | 41 | 64 |
| N | (39) | (169) | (199) |

$X^2 = 24.93$, $p < .001$

they ever used that right. As Table 13 shows, those who used no outside services tended to be satisfied, not wanting to change their Medical Group doctors. But the patients who used outside

---

[1] Some of the questions used here and in other portions of the Montefiore Medical Group survey were adapted from Survey 367 of the National Opinion Research Center (the NORC-HIF study). See footnote on p. 35.

Some comparisons on these items between the Montefiore Medical Group subscribers and a national sample might be useful: 17 per cent of the national sample reported going to a second doctor to get his opinion without telling the first, compared to 31 per cent of the subscribers; 29 per cent of the national sample reported they "stopped going to a doctor" because of dissatisfaction, compared to 47 per cent of the subscribers.

In this regard we might note that Earl Koos in *Health in Regionville* (Columbia University Press, New York, 1954, pp. 60 ff.) reported that 13 per cent of his rural sample "dropped" a doctor. Michael Balint in *The Doctor, His Patient and the Illness* (International Universities Press, New York, 1957, p. 264) reports his impression that from "eight to ten per cent of the patients on a [London] doctor's list change their doctors in any one year."

services, whether regularly or occasionally, were both dissatisfied to a similar degree: the difference was that the occasional user tried to do something about it by asking for a change, while the regular user merely wished he could change.

The regular user of outside services may not exercise his rights as a HIP subscriber because he is committed to the services he obtains outside, not because he is by nature passive. We find, in fact, that he, more than the other patients, is attached to the physician whom he used before subscribing to HIP. As we see in Table 14, 72 per cent of the regular users of outside services answered the question, "When you joined HIP were you sorry

TABLE 14. USE OF OUTSIDE SERVICES AND ATTACHMENT TO PRIOR REGULAR DOCTOR
(Patients enrolled in HIP more than four years)

| "When you joined HIP were you sorry to leave your regular, non-HIP doctor?" | Regular users of outside services | Occasional users of outside services | Nonusers of outside services |
|---|---|---|---|
| | *Per cent* | | |
| Answers indicating attachment[a] | 72 | 58 | 32 |
| "No, not sorry to leave him" | 9 | 14 | 24 |
| "Had no regular doctor before HIP" | 19 | 28 | 44 |
| N | (42) | (169) | (204) |

$X^2 = 34.75$, p < .001
[a] These answers were, "Yes, sorry to leave him," and "No, because we kept him anyway."

to leave your regular non-HIP doctor?" either positively or by indicating that they "kept him anyway." Fifty-eight per cent of the occasional outside users indicated attachment to their prior doctor, but this was true of only 32 per cent of those who used no outside services. Indeed, of those regular outside users who were subscribers for more than four years, 71 per cent, almost three-fourths, indicated that the doctor they used for most medical needs was one they knew before joining HIP.

Table 14 suggests that those who regularly used the services of an outside physician had had satisfactory experience with entrepreneurial practice before joining HIP. It also suggests that those who used *no* outside services had *not* had very satisfactory experience. Largely on the lower end of the social scale, many had had no regular contacts with medical practitioners except, we may presume, in public or quasi-public clinics.[1] One would gather from examination of the evaluations of medical care in the preceding tables that if those who regularly used the services of outside physicians constitute a minority which had had particularly satisfying experience with solo practitioners, those who never used outside services constitute a majority which had *not*.

## Patients and Utilization of Outside Medical Services

We may summarize the material by sketching a picture of each type of patient. The patient who, after being a subscriber in the Montefiore Medical Group for some time, still does not use any outside physician tends to be of the lower educational and occupational levels, without much sensitivity about his status in a medical care program. On the whole, he is rather passive in his view of medical care, generally taking what he gets without much question, but he does tend to feel that he is getting better care and attention from the Medical Group than he received from entrepreneurial physicians or the clinics to which he went for help before becoming a HIP subscriber. Having had little experience with outside services, lacking a very critical attitude toward medical care, and ill-equipped to pay double fees, he is the loyal backbone of the Medical Group.

The patient who, after being enrolled for some time in the Montefiore Medical Group, finds occasion to use the services of an entrepreneurial physician, but who nonetheless uses the Medical Group for most of his medical needs, tends to be of the higher educational and occupational level. As such, he has a somewhat different conception of self from the majority of patients. Confronted with much the same stimuli as the others, he seems more likely to perceive insult, or the self-deprecating overtones of being treated like a "charity case," for he has a higher and, therefore, more vulnerable status than the others.

---

[1] Odin W. Anderson and Paul B. Sheatsley in *Comprehensive Medical Insurance* (Health Information Foundation Research Series, no. 9, 1959, p. 47) note that "a significantly larger proportion of HIP enrollees had received most or some of their care at clinics" prior to joining HIP.

His attitude toward medical care and medical care systems seems
to be active and critical rather than passive and accepting, for
he tends to have "shopped around," to have dared to assess the
physician's competence, and to have switched doctors more than
most patients. That this response is rational and manipulative
rather than evasive, is suggested by the fact that he has asked to
change his HIP physician under the terms of his contract privilege. On the whole, he assesses favorably the care he receives
from the Montefiore Medical Group, but he tends to be more
detached than committed, more equivocal than positive. He
tends to feel that the care he gets from the Medical Group is as
good as, rather than better than, what he received previously.
Fairly familiar with "outside" medical facilities, financially
equipped to use them without hardship, he goes outside when he
thinks it necessary.

The subscribers who regularly use the services of an entrepreneurial physician for most of their medical needs are predis-
posed to reject HIP services. While we cannot say that new
individual subscribers who use outside services regularly will
continue to do so no matter how long they are enrolled (some
of the case histories testify to the transient state of regular outside
use), the proportion of that type of subscriber does not vary with
time in the Group. And these patients have no distinct tendency
to be in one social class or another. They are distinct only in their
extreme criticism of the care they receive in the Montefiore
Medical Group and approval of the care they received before
joining HIP. Indeed, we may say that they are committed to an
outside solo practitioner. It is unwise, however, to assume that the
regular outside user's commitment to a solo practitioner has any
necessarily strong emotional component. In the next chapter,
when we examine the circumstances in which outside utilization
took place, we will see that the psychological characteristics of the
doctor-patient relationship may not be so important an attraction as the way the doctor's practice fits into the patient's scheme
of things.

# 7. Choice Between Practices and the Lay Referral System

THE SIXTY-TWO SUBSCRIBERS who reported using outside surgical or obstetrical services for other than the technical reasons described in the preceding chapter were asked not only what particular service they sought, but also why they went outside to obtain it. Almost all their explanations can be classified into either one of two categories.

In one class, outside utilization occurred not because there was any dissatisfaction with, or suspicion of, the HIP medical group, but because the patient had developed confidence in an outside physician and, having had no occasion to become acquainted with the HIP surgeon or obstetrician, preferred to use the physician whom he already knew or with whose reputation he was familiar. In this class fell such explanations as "My last delivery, before I joined HIP, was difficult, and I felt my old doctor knew my case, so I went to him for my next baby even though I was then in HIP"; or "I didn't know the HIP man and I was already under the care of a friend"; or for "ulcer surgery, I know some people who were cured by a private doctor so I went to him." None of these explanations involved any direct rejection of the Medical Group or its services. Together, they constituted somewhat more than half of the 63 instances of outside utilization of surgical-obstetrical services.[1]

Twenty-six of the remaining explanations—41 per cent of all explanations—referred not to prior familiarity with, and confidence in, some outside surgeon or obstetrician, but to experi-

[1] One of the 62 subscribers reported two instances of utilization of outside surgical-obstetrical services.

133

ences in HIP that led to loss of confidence in its services.[1] Outside utilization occurred only *after* the patient believed he suffered from rudeness on the part of the doctor or from a misdiagnosis. One woman used outside medical service for her second delivery because she believed that her attending HIP obstetrician was responsible for the death of her first child. Another, who went outside for a hysterectomy, wrote that her HIP physician frightened her by saying that she might have a malignant growth: she reported that before operating, her "own" outside doctor assured her this was not so. Another, with "tumors on her breast," wrote that she had been going to a HIP surgeon for seven weeks for observation, but finally became disgusted, went to her "old" doctor, and on his advice and that of four other outside doctors had the tumors removed successfully. Another reported her HIP gynecologist to be "unsympathetic and sarcastic" and had her cervix cauterized by an outside surgeon.

### Outside Use of Medical Services

Why do patients use outside *medical* services? Not controlling for the length of time the respondent has been a subscriber (since this was not possible for the use of outside surgical-obstetrical services), but eliminating instances explained by contract coverage or on-the-job care (as we eliminated similar reasons for the use of outside surgical-obstetrical services), we may directly compare the proportions of reasons given for each type of outside utilization. There are some interesting differences.

Few subscribers seem to have used outside medical services solely because of their familiarity with an outside doctor. Compared to the 55 per cent of those explaining their use of outside surgical-obstetrical services by their familiarity with an outside doctor, only 14 per cent offered that explanation for using outside medical services. They checked the answer, "Used to the non-HIP doctor and didn't want to try HIP doctors," and wrote in that the old doctor was a personal friend,

---

[1] In this light, then, only 4 per cent of the Montefiore Medical Group subscribers reported outside utilization of surgical or obstetrical services for reasons that were actually critical of HIP or the Medical Group.

or that they were new to HIP and had confidence in their former doctors, or that, in the words of a schoolteacher, "My old doctor knows me and my family thoroughly." Attraction outside without any "push" from unsatisfactory experience with HIP care is thus important in a far smaller proportion of cases for medical than for surgical-obstetrical services.

What *is* important is accessibility. Thirty-seven per cent of the reasons referred to the accessibility of services. About half of these stressed some element of convenience, examples of which are such written-in-answers as, "Because house-calls take so long, I see my old doctor for immediate care when it's necessary," "It's convenient—he lives across the street," and "I can get an appointment quicker." No necessarily negative judgment of the quality of care available from the HIP medical group is involved nor, for that matter, any particularly positive judgment of the quality of care outside. The other half of the reasons involving the criterion of accessibility stressed "emergency" care, which also involves no necessarily invidious judgment of quality of care but only considerations of time and space. The need for care is perceived and the most quickly or easily available source of services is believed to be an outside physician. A few reasons not covered by "convenience" or "emergency" referred to perceived inability to get an appointment with a HIP group.

Finally, 49 per cent of the reasons given for the use of outside medical services—a somewhat greater proportion than was the case for surgical or obstetrical services—involved dissatisfaction that led to at least the temporary rejection of HIP services.[1] Three per cent checked "Don't feel HIP doctors are very good." Twenty-four per cent checked "Don't feel HIP doctors are interested enough." Six per cent wrote in reasons expressing lack of confidence, such as "No faith in HIP" and "Lack of confidence in HIP doctors due to their indifferent clinic treatment." Another 6 per cent indicated that they went outside to "confirm a diagnosis." And, finally, 10 per cent wrote in reasons that expressed

---

[1] Thus, about 23 per cent of the Montefiore Medical Group subscribers reported outside utilization of medical services for reasons that were actually critical of HIP or the Medical Group.

dissatisfaction with specific services—for example, "keeping a child's burn bandaged without changing bandage for six weeks," "no cure," "failed to treat me for hemorrhoids," "HIP doctors haven't been able to diagnose my case," and "phone diagnosis and prescription."

The contrast between the reasons given for the use of outside surgical-obstetrical services and for the use of outside medical services emphasizes what should be obvious but is too easily forgotten. While people of much the same socioeconomic characteristics and attitudes are involved in both cases, the circumstances surrounding outside utilization may emphasize one feature of experience in one case and quite another feature in the other. One might expect confidence in, or familiarity with, an outside physician to be an important consideration in surgery or obstetrics, for anxiety is likely to pervade the use of those services. When more routine and varied medical care is involved, however, a considerably smaller proportion of patients is motivated by positive personal attraction to an individual.

Bearing in mind the importance of circumstance, we may recall the "attachment" of regular users of outside medical services to an entrepreneurial physician. When we inspect their reasons for their outside utilization, we see that their attachment seems casual rather than laden with affect. Table 15 shows that while there is not much difference between the proportion of regular and occasional users of outside services who go outside

TABLE 15. REASONS FOR USING OUTSIDE SERVICES, BY TYPE OF UTILIZATION

(Patients enrolled in HIP more than four years)

| Reasons for using outside physician | Regular users of an outside physician | Occasional users of an outside physician |
|---|---|---|
| | Per cent | |
| Familiarity with outside doctor | 14 | 16 |
| Dissatisfaction with HIP | 27 | 57 |
| Accessibility of outside doctor | 59 | 27 |
| N | (44) | (159) |

$X^2 = 17.22$, p < .001

because of their familiarity with their old doctor, the regular outside users much more often stress the *accessibility* of the entrepreneurial practitioner as their reason.[1] The occasional outside users stress experiences with HIP that have actively repelled them. Thus, it does not seem to be the doctor-patient relationship that is responsible for the regular use of outside services so much as the *accommodation of the practice of the entrepreneurial physician to the personal affairs of the patient.*

### Routine and Crisis in Outside Utilization

Implied in our discussion thus far is a distinction between circumstances in which the prospective patient perceives his problem to be serious and critical, and those in which he perceives it to be routine and merely technical. In the former fall pregnancy, symptoms seeming to call for surgery, and illnesses that involve either pain or the threat of severe social or physical incapacitation. In the latter fall symptoms that are annoying but not painful or incapacitating, a prime example of which is the common cold. The former tend to involve much anxiety, the latter little.

Crisis and routine cannot be defined precisely by specific symptoms, however, for the variable culture of the patient mediates between the symptom and his response. While pregnancy and child delivery were not seen by any patient to be completely routine matters, the upper-middle class women who were interviewed seemed to manifest much less anxiety about them than the lower-middle and lower class patients. Of those who indicated the use of outside surgical-obstetrical services, 35 per cent of the instances reported by patients with some college

---

[1] It may be felt that to combine "emergency," "couldn't get an appointment at HIP," and "convenience" in the one category of "accessibility" is unwarranted. Taking "convenience" alone as the basis of comparison, however, a similar pattern is obtained: familiarity with the outside doctor was stressed by 20 per cent of the regular outside users and 18 per cent of the occasional; deficiencies of HIP were stressed by 40 per cent of the regular outside users and 64 per cent of the occasional; the accessibility of the outside practitioner was stressed by 40 per cent of the regular outside users and 18 per cent of the occasional.

It is interesting to note that the reason of "emergency" is given less often, and "convenience" more often as the length of time the respondent has been a subscriber increases. Citation of "emergency" varies inversely with education while citation of "convenience" varies directly.

training were for child delivery compared to 50 per cent reported by women who have had no more than a high school education.

The definition of crisis and routine seems to vary not only according to the patient's understanding of the symptoms but also according to the status of the person manifesting the symptoms. Crudely put, pregnancy in an unmarried teenager warrants considerably more affect than pregnancy in a thirty-five-year-old mother of three. And the symptoms of a "cold" in a child during the polio season occasion more anxiety than the same symptoms in an adult during the same period. In The Bronx, sickness in a child is less likely to be treated matter-of-factly than sickness in an adult irrespective of social class, for there is no difference between the college-educated and the less-than-college-educated groups in the proportion of instances of use of outside surgical services in which children were involved, nor was there any important difference by education in the proportion of use by children of outside medical services.

The definitions of crisis and routine involve different attitudes toward medical services, attitudes not necessarily manifested from day to day. When a crisis is perceived, a great deal of concern about the competence of the practitioner often arises. The same person on one occasion can assume that any physician at all is competent to treat a routine disorder and on another occasion, in which a crisis is perceived, worry about the competence of a physician. In a situation of crisis it matters a great deal who the physician is, and time and money are no object. In a situation of routine it is not of great importance who the physician is, but how conveniently he can be reached and how much he charges are important. In the latter case the organization of practice plays a more important role than in the former.

The difference between the two circumstances may be illustrated by the case of an upper-lower class Italian family that has used a great many outside services. When interviewed, the husband and wife considered themselves loyal supporters of HIP and had no complaint other than the difficulty of getting house-calls. When they first belonged to HIP, however, they never used the services of the Medical Group, preferring to use the services of the

neighborhood doctor whose patients they were before they joined
the plan. "He's just wonderful," said the wife. "He'd come over
within ten minutes any time of day or night." When the wife had
her first baby, she used her neighborhood physician for him,
without even trying to use the pediatric services of the Medical
Group. Once, however, the baby got sick and the physician (who
was not a pediatrician) was puzzled by the symptoms and treated
them without success. On his own initiative he telephoned to a
pediatrician at the Medical Group and asked him to come to see
the baby. The Medical Group physician, reported the parents,
diagnosed the ailment as roseola, and in the best Hippocratic
tradition made a detailed prognosis that was confirmed by later
events. From that time on the family—adults and child—used
Medical Group services by day but continued to call their
neighborhood physician for house-calls at night.

After a time this family joined the Family Health Maintenance
Demonstration. They still continued to use the neighborhood
physician for night house-calls even though their enthusiasm for
the Demonstration knew no bounds. On one occasion while
enrolled in the Demonstration, the pediatrician recommended
corrective surgery for one of the children. Panicked by the
thought of surgery on their child, the husband and wife con-
ferred with the wife's parents and then decided to consult an
outside doctor. The first one they consulted agreed that surgery
was necessary; they saw a second, who also agreed on the necessity of surgery; the third said that surgery was probably the only
thing to correct the condition but agreed nonetheless to try less
"drastic" measures and to watch the condition carefully to see
whether it might "correct itself." The parents went to him two
or three times a week at first, then weekly, and then every two
weeks for about a year, with apparently inconclusive results. All
this time they continued to take their children to the Demonstration pediatrician for "routine care."

The same family used outside physicians for both routine care
and crises. In one instance they did not take advantage of their
contract benefits because they were accustomed to their old
neighborhood doctor and they liked him. When they found they

could get competent and tolerably pleasant care from the Medical Group, however, they began using it.[1] Inasmuch as they found it difficult to get night house-calls from the Medical Group, they regularly used their old doctor for that service. An important element in this sort of "routine" outside use was the accessibility of a neighborhood physician. There was no particular question of competence involved. In the crisis a different element was present. The physician's diagnosis and prescription were in question. The family shopped around until they found a physician who would consider an agreeable prescription. Outside utilization involved not a convenient doctor, but one willing to go along with the patient's opinion about treatment.

### Clashes of Lay and Medical Opinion

While differences of opinion between patient and doctor are more striking in circumstances in which the patient perceives a crisis, they also occur in routine affairs. Indeed, we may range "differences of opinion" along a continuum. At one end is self-treatment, for self-treatment involves rejection of a medical practice even though it does not involve choosing an alternative practice. In self-treatment which follows consultation, the patient assumes that his opinion or his ability is essentially as good as, if not better than, that of the physician he consults; and if the physician does not agree with the self-diagnosis the patient proceeds to go "outside" to treat himself. A simple case of this was an upper-lower class housewife who felt "anemic" and in need of a "tonic." When she consulted her Demonstration doctor he tried without success to convince her, after tests and examination, that vitamin "tonics" would do her no good. She dosed herself. Several upper-lower class men in the Demonstration could not be induced to submit to patch tests to determine the

---

[1] Their attachment to their old doctor was no greater than the attachment of others interviewed, in that as much as they liked him they switched to the Medical Group with few if any qualms. All the empirical evidence of this study, in fact, indicates that the strength of patients' emotional attachment to their physicians has been greatly exaggerated by the literature on medical practice and the doctor-patient relationship. That patients become emotionally involved on occasion is indubitable, and that something resembling a psychotherapeutic climate during treatment may emerge is true, but it does not follow from this that those occasions are generalized into a persistent and strong sense of personal loyalty to a particular physician. The whole subject needs careful, unsentimental investigation.

"cause" of their allergic reactions, for they were satisfied that their own experiments with avoiding particular foods and substances had successfully located the "cause."

A similar situation exists when the physician's prescription is partially accepted but is "too much bother" to follow. This may be illustrated by the case of an upper-lower class husband afflicted with what he described as "funny skin and nails" on his hands. He consulted a Medical Group dermatologist, who painted the skin and nails with something, and told him to come every week for treatment. The patient asked why he could not paint his hands himself rather than have the bother of reporting for treatment. The dermatologist answered that he wanted to observe and record any changes that took place. The patient, determined to avoid the weekly visit, and unimpressed with the necessity of continued observation, went to a druggist and asked for silver nitrate. He said he was sure the medication was silver nitrate because it turned his nails black. The druggist discouraged him by indicating that it would be dangerous to experiment without knowing the concentration of the solution.

Vitamins, tonics, and silver nitrate do not require a physician's prescription. When the patient believes that such medicaments would help him even though advised to the contrary by a physician, he is able to buy them himself and treat himself. For drugs that do require a physician's prescription, however, the outside service he seeks must be professional. The patient must find a physician who agrees with him, or at least who is willing to humor him. An instance of this was reported by a lower-middle class male who had bronchitis and who "knew it responds very well to penicillin." He went to his Family Doctor at the Medical Group, told him he had bronchitis, and asked for penicillin. The physician refused, recommending instead another mode of treatment. The patient left and went to his former physician who, he reported, "knows me," and reported that he got "ten shots" of penicillin from him. If, as is reported to be the case in rural Greece,[1] penicillin were sold without prescription,

[1] See Friedl, Ernestine, "Hospital Care in Provincial Greece," *Human Organization*, vol. 16, Winter, 1958, pp. 24–27.

the patient would hardly have bothered going to an outside physician—he would simply have bought what he felt he needed. Thus, just as a necessary condition for self-treatment rests on access to proper drugs and devices, so a necessary condition for this second sort of outside utilization rests on the availability of physicians who share or are willing to go along with the patient's conception of treatment.

In all of the instances discussed so far we have not found indignation in the patient's response. None of the instances initiated outright rejection of Medical Group services or physicians. However, at the extreme end of the spectrum of differences of opinion the patient believes that a serious error is being made, or that he is not getting the attention his case warrants. Rather than a "you go your way, I'll go mine" attitude, he feels a sense of outrage. He believes that he must have the services of another physician for the "proper" care, and he goes outside blaming the Group for the persistence of his illness.

### The Career of Illness

But patients' opinions about their illness do not exist in a vacuum. In the consulting-room their opinions may seem self-sufficient, but they are in reality formed by events outside the doctor's office. One important element contributing to the formation of lay opinions about illness, to the tenacity with which they are held, and to the decision to reject a doctor's opinion is the influence on the patient of other laymen. The importance of lay interpersonal influence for the way the patient looks at his illness is suggested by examination of the process through which a complaint is perceived and managed.

A complaint may last many years. If it is only intermittent and not severely incapacitating, it may never be defined as an illness worthy of the attention of so important a person as a doctor. Both the potential length and uncertainty of defining a complaint may be illustrated by an upper-middle class husband's case history.

When the husband was in the Army he had a "cold" that lasted several weeks. After observing the symptoms for a few days, the man's wife insisted that the ailment could not be a cold—it must be an allergy and he should see a doctor. The husband felt that his wife was wrong and he refused to consult a doctor for treatment of a mere cold.[1] The symptoms persisted for six or seven weeks and then vanished. The husband was discharged from the Army the following year and returned to civilian work. During that second year he again had a "cold" which lasted several weeks. His wife again insisted that he must have hay fever. She reminded him that in a conversation about it his uncle—a physician—also said he must be suffering from an allergy, and she finally persuaded him to consult a physician who was a friend of theirs. The physician-friend diagnosed the ailment as a cold and joked about the wife's diagnostic qualifications. Eventually the "cold" disappeared. During the third year the husband began sneezing again and his wife insisted that he consult another doctor. This time hay fever was diagnosed and the symptoms were henceforth controlled.

The case history above shows that a complaint is dealt with by a succession of distinct steps. The first step is tentative self-diagnosis—perceiving the complaint as a cold. In assessing the complaint, its duration was more significant than the perceived physical symptoms—when the "cold" did not disappear within a few days, it became something to which rather special attention was directed. At the very least, then, the prescription called for by the first step of lay diagnosis was to wait, however briefly, to see if the symptoms would disappear. It may also consist of more active measures like staying in bed for a day or so and taking aspirin. If the complaint disappears, attention to it fades.

The case history also shows that during the early stage of perceiving an illness, the patient does not necessarily form an opinion by himself. The first physician consulted about the cold symptoms had to deprecate the wife's diagnostic qualifications, not the patient's. It was commonly reported in the interviews that mutual consultation often took place within the household before a doctor was called. Certainly it does not always take place. Available data are sketchy, but they suggest that consultation between husband and wife is most likely to take place when the

[1] For us, in the middle of the twentieth century, the "common cold" is a minor annoyance that must be put up with passively as a fact of life. This is likely to be as amusing to those following us as is now to us the casual way in which illnesses like malaria and gonorrhea were treated in the past.

individual's ailment appears to be relatively marked—for example, a real cold rather than a passing stuffy nose or a smoker's cough—and when the ailment is one about which husband and wife can talk freely—for example, muscular pain rather than menstrual disorders. When interaction goes on between members of the immediate family the definition of the complaint and its disposition are significantly affected. If the spouse agrees that the illness is significant, a physician is more likely to be consulted quickly than if the spouse disagrees. Some patients reported that when a child was ill one of the parents, usually the husband, had the regular role of soothing the other and delaying the request for a physician's services.

It is easy to underestimate the significance of lay influence in the utilization of medical care or to overlook it entirely. Commiseration and helpful suggestion, trading symptoms and experiences, gossip about doctors and medical institutions, these are an ubiquitous part of everyday life. But to study interpersonal influence[1] is about as difficult as to study such routine and unwitting behavior as coughing and yawning—one finds it as hard to recall accurately all the recent occasions on which he coughed or yawned as to recall accurately the occasions on which he discussed babies and pediatricians, wives and gynecologists, early morning stiffness and rheum, "flu" and viruses. It is only the marked instance that stands out in one's memory.

In perhaps the majority of instances reported in the interviews (though the true universe of instances is so uncertain that quantitative statements are bound to be rhetorical), lay consultation did not take place outside the household. When a baby had a temperature and acted as though he was in pain, none of the parents shopped around for the opinions of friends or relatives before calling a doctor. A large variety of complaints seemed sufficiently self-evident or pressing to require that the doctor be called immediately after the household consultation. However, when the complaint was not pressing or self-evident, and the

---

[1] For specification of its significance to other areas of American life, see Katz, Elihu and Paul F. Lazarsfeld, *Personal Influence*, The Free Press, Glencoe, Ill., 1955; and Katz, Elihu, "The Two-Step Flow of Communication: An Up-to-Date Report on an Hypothesis," *Public Opinion Quarterly*, vol. 21, Spring, 1957, pp. 61–78.

members of the household could not decide what to do, consultation with laymen *outside* the household tended to occur. A lower class housewife had a pain in her leg for several months. She and her husband could not decide to see a doctor. As the pain increased, she began consulting her relatives. One suggested an orthopedic hospital. After thinking the situation over, she decided to call her regular physician first, but finding that he was out of town she asked a referral service to send a physician. The medication he gave her was ineffective and his manner annoying, so she then went to the orthopedic hospital. In other cases, particularly those involving diffuse complaints like interpersonal problems and allergies, lay consultants tended to deprecate the complaint by calling it normal or minor, and so discouraged consultation with a professional practitioner.

We have seen that the first step in the history of a patient's complaint is self-diagnosis, followed by confirmation or alteration of the diagnosis when he consults others in his household. No further steps may be taken if the lay diagnosis so indicates and the complaint is bearable. If doing something about the complaint is suggested by the self-diagnosis, however, the next step is likely to be self-treatment. If the indisposition continues, friends and relatives may be consulted, but the most common next step is to consult a physician. However, seeing a physician does not necessarily end consultation with laymen. After the patient obtains a professional diagnosis and prescription, he may turn to his lay consultants for advice even if he had not done so before seeing the physician. Sometimes he is led to seek an additional practitioner for "better" treatment. In one case an upper-lower-class housewife discovered a cyst on her breast. She went to her Family Health Maintenance Demonstration doctor, who referred her to a Medical Group surgeon. The surgeon examined her and told her to come back in two weeks: he wanted to observe changes in the cyst before deciding to operate. No treatment was prescribed in the meantime. While discussing her experience with friends, one of them told her that she had had the very same problem and a solo practitioner gave her injections which effected a cure. The patient immediately went to that "outside" physician for injections. In another case an upper-lower class housewife had a stiff neck and went to her Family Health Maintenance Demonstration physician for treatment. She reported that he merely said she should relax, take it easy, and the stiffness would subside. It did not subside. Soon thereafter she mentioned her difficulty to a friend, who promptly referred her to a "wonderful" chiropractor. The patient went to the chiropractor for several weeks and her complaint disappeared.

## The Lay Referral System

Examination of the history of complaints shows us that there is a set of rather definite steps through which the patient goes in handling his illness. The steps constitute stages of forming an opinion about the nature of the complaint and what to do about it. Consultation with other laymen is often crucial to the opinion that is formed and subsequent consultation with professional practitioners. The concept of the lay referral system may be used to analyze the events that occur during the history of a complaint.

The concept of the lay referral system is predicated not on a set of attributes that an individual may possess, but on a career, a patterned sequence of events through which individuals pass. In a career the individual responds to a set of organized alternatives which are given by the social structure. The individual selects one or another alternative, each of which, like a turn in a maze or a move in a game, tends to restrict future choices.

The doctor is but one consultant of many, and the patient often arrives at his office only after having exhausted a whole network of less formal consultants. The *lay referral structure* is one part of the lay referral system and consists in a network of consultants, potential or actual, running from the intimate and most informal confines of the nuclear family through successively more select, distant, and authoritative persons until the "professional" is reached. It is a network of referrals in that consultants not only diagnose and prescribe but also make referrals. The network imposes form on the process of seeking help and is organized independently of the interconnections among professionals and professional institutions.[1] Interaction with nonprofessional consultants in the lay referral structure is just as responsible for the patient's not following the doctor's orders or not returning for further treatment as are the cessation of symptoms and the patient's personal opinions about proper treatment.

Aside from the network of consultant positions, another element of the lay referral system is the culture or education of its participants. Obviously relevant are the norms surrounding the sick role, the conception of illness, its causes and its cures, and the norms surrounding the consultant role. These norms underlie the "differences of opinion" that lead to self-treatment or to the use of an "outside" doctor. By definition they vary from culture to culture, as well as from subculture to subculture.

## Contrasting Lay Referral Systems

In The Bronx the lower class patient seems to participate in a lay referral system that differs from that of the upper-middle class patient.[2] Some class differences have already been suggested by the contrast between those who occasionally use outside medical services and those who use none. There was difference in status sensitivity—one seemed more prone to feel insulted and to feel like a charity case than the other. There was a difference in the approach to medical care—one seemed more active, subjecting the care he gets to continuous scrutiny, more likely to be critical than the other. And there was difference in experience with solo practitioners—one was more likely than the other to have had a regular doctor prior to enrollment in the Health Insurance Plan.

[1] There will be occasion later to refer to the *professional referral system*. Like the lay referral system, it rests upon a set of norms shared by the participating consultants, and consists in a hierarchy of diagnostic authority. Unlike the lay referral system, however, it tends to be organized independently of the layman and his understandings. It is controlled much more by the professional workers than by the patient seeking help, and tends to be independent of any cohesive group of patients. The lay and professional systems intersect at the point in which professional workers have a position in the lay system. The patient penetrates the professional referral system when he contacts an institution or professional worker that would not be accessible to him without a professional referral.

[2] The contrast made statistically, unless otherwise indicated, is between college graduates and those who have not been graduated from high school; between professional, semi-professional and executive workers, and semi-skilled workers.

The responses of lower class patients to illness—women more than men, but men as well—seemed to be timid and fearful. Pregnancy and childbirth were surrounded with mystery and fear for many of the lower class women interviewed. Where half of the lower class women who were interviewed stressed their "fright," their "not knowing what to expect," and their need for a soothing, paternal obstetrician, none of the upper-middle class women did. The lower class mother tended to be embarrassed by bodily functions, particularly her own. One lower class woman with rectal bleeding refused a proposed proctoscopy because it was too "intimate." Both husbands and wives of five of the lower class families that had regular doctors prior to enrollment, mentioned that they did not use HIP services for some time after joining because they did not know what they were entitled to from the Medical Group and were reluctant to explore the new and unknown situation. And some of them who had been patients of a local doctor before they joined HIP said they were "afraid" to call him later—one housewife saying that after she was discharged from the Family Health Maintenance Demonstration she wanted to drop HIP entirely, but hesitated to go back to her former doctor because he disapproved of her joining HIP. Many lower class mothers said that they were "afraid" to ask the doctor questions, or to bring up such problems as "nervousness" for fear of being laughed at. Neither they nor their husbands tended to feel that they had any legitimate "rights" as patients. Seeing a doctor was not an everyday, relaxed affair for them. They feared rebuff and anticipated the accusation that they were wasting the doctor's time or "bothering him."

Both apprehension about illness and timidity about consulting a doctor are rooted in the very real ignorance the lower class patients displayed about illness and, in particular, modes of diagnosis and treatment. Ignorance seemed particularly marked for the more ambiguous complaints, allergies, gastro-intestinal disorders, musculo-skeletal, and, even more particularly, psychosomatic or "nervous" problems. They were likely to accept those complaints as inevitable and to have received medical treatment for them almost by accident. They seemed to have very limited

knowledge of what it is physicians do—beyond taking patients'
blood pressure, giving blood tests and injections, making urin-
alyses, and taking x-rays; they can only talk vaguely. The
few lower class patients who were dissatisfied with the way their
illness was being treated could not say anything more than that
they "ought to be doing more about it." Their fearfulness and
ignorance sometimes erupted into severe agitation. When this
occurred they were inclined to go outside the Medical Group.
More often, their behavior in the Medical Group was rather
passive.

The upper-middle class patient is considerably more detached,
active, and informed in his relationship to medical care. While he
may be initially just interested in learning what it is the doctor
does and why, he later uses his accumulated knowledge to assess
what was or was not done to him. One woman, for example,
learned what a "blood coag" test was and its purpose when it was
ordered for her child. A few weeks later her child had a tonsill-
ectomy and "hemorrhaged a great deal," at which point her
husband wondered whether a "blood coag" test should not have
been made immediately before the operation as well as three
weeks before.

Upper-middle class patients seem to be able to take a detached
view of their bodies, seeing themselves and their illness with a
kind of academic interest.[1] Perhaps because of this, they more
easily share the clinical perspective of the physician than does the
lower class patient. Rather than simple, anxious submission to
examination and treatment there is, as one woman put it, "a
personal need to know what I'm doing and why I'm doing it,"
before submission is granted. This "need" is, of course, hardly
peculiar to the upper-middle class patient—in one way or another most patients are likely to want to be told something about
their condition and its treatment—but the upper-middle class
patient is assertive enough to demand satisfaction, and his
satisfaction hinges on receiving fairly elaborate and technical

[1] See, for example, Schatzman, Leonard, and Anselm Strauss, "Social Class and
Modes of Communication," *American Journal of Sociology*, vol. 60, January, 1955,
pp. 329–338.

information. The upper-middle class patient asks for a relationship that is near that of a colleague rather than a patient, near that of an equal rather than a subordinate.

It is not only his level of information or the level of his demand for information that is involved in the upper-middle class patient's attitude to physicians; it is also the status he brings into the consulting-room. The physician is not of such exceptionally high prestige that he is remote from the upper-middle class patient's everyday life. He is, indeed, an expert (just as the patient may himself be an expert in some other field), but he is also a person with very much the same general education and standard of living as the patient himself. In fact, he may be a friend or a relative of the patient. Thus, the upper-middle class patient and his physician are equals outside the consulting-room, a fact that seems to be difficult to suppress even when the patient is ridiculously naked, stripped of the vestments of his position in the community. The upper-middle class patient thus feels considerably fewer social restraints operating in his interaction with the physician.

Cultural differences between the lower and the upper-middle class lay referral systems are complemented by differences in referral structure. The lower class system might be called *parochial* both because of the limitation of its culture and the limitation of its structural connections with medical institutions. Neither the lower class patient nor his lay consultants are very familiar with the range of medical services available in The Bronx and in Manhattan. Very often the patient has had no regular contact with an individual physician, and whatever contact he has had with any source of medical care has been limited. Public or quasi-public clinics being what they are, the only source of medical care which he is likely to feel he can use freely is the neighborhood practitioner. He and his consultants lack both the knowledge and the aggressiveness necessary for free utilization of all other alternatives. Symptomatic of the limitation of lower class contacts with medicine is the finding that 87 per cent of the outside users in the least educated group reported the use of a physician whom they knew before joining HIP. As education increased, the percentage dropped smoothly to 58 per cent of the outside users in the best-educated group.

The influence of the lower class referral system on the individual patient is intensified by its cohesiveness and his dependence upon it. It tends to be localized. In a Family Health Maintenance Demonstration survey, 76 per cent of the 83 lower class patients responding indicated that they had lived in their neighborhood for six years or more, compared to 46 per cent of 71 upper-middle class respondents. Furthermore, their kin and friends tended to live in the same neighborhood—56 per cent reported their parents living close by (compared to 37 per cent of the upper-middle class patients), 69 per cent reported other relatives living close by (compared to 57 per cent of the upper-middle class patients), and 78 per cent reported some of their "really close friends" living nearby (compared to 56 per cent of the upper-middle class patients). Reports of frequent (at least weekly) association with kin and friends show smaller differences between the classes, but in no case do they fail to show more of the lower than the upper-middle class reporting frequent association with parents, relatives, and close friends.

In contrast, the upper-middle class patient participates in what might be called a *cosmopolitan* system. The interviews show that he is markedly more prone to make decisions about medical care himself, without the aid of lay consultants outside the household. More familiar with abstract criteria of professional qualifications, better acquainted with a number of practices if only by his changes of residence, and more knowledgeable about illness itself, he is likely to feel more secure in his own diagnosis and his own assessment of a physician's virtues. He therefore has less need of lay consultation than the lower class patient. However, if he should ask help from his potential lay consultants who are scattered about the city and as knowledgeable as he, they are likely to extend immeasurably his contacts with alternative sources of diagnosis and treatment, and sophisticated modes of evaluating them.

# 8. The Role of the Organization of Practice

THE PATIENTS GAVE THREE PRIME REASONS for the use of outside services. First, important for the use of outside surgery and obstetrics, is prior familiarity with, or confidence in, a physician. In the crisis of surgery or childbirth, some patients felt it prudent to use someone who "knows" them and who has treated them satisfactorily in the past. Second, important for the use of outside medical services, is the emergency accessibility or the routine convenience of the practice. Third, important for the use of both outside surgical-obstetrical and medical services, is dissatisfaction with Group services—often a product of the clash of lay and professional expectations. To each of these reasons there are two sides. One is the patient's disposition to behave in a particular way. We have seen that the upper-middle class patient is more likely than lower class patients to seek outside medical services because he is more likely to have had regular, familiarizing experience with solo practitioners, more likely to be willing and able to pay extra for convenience, and more active and critical in assessing the care he gets. The other side remains to be discussed —the way the organization of practice stimulates or limits the choices which patients make, and bears on the accessibility, familiarity, and compatibility of doctors.

## Contrasts in the Rationalization of Services

In both the Family Health Maintenance Demonstration and the Montefiore Medical Group, if the patient wants the care to which he is entitled by his contract, he must use physicians or services that are party to his contract. This limitation commits him to an organization of services that is markedly different from the entrepreneurial system of practice. Both the Montefiore Medical Group and the Family Health Maintenance Demonstration operate in a central medical group building where all personnel have their consulting-rooms and offices. By and large, it is to this building that the patient must go if he wants care, or from this building that the physician must sally if he is to make a house-call. Given the densely populated area being served, travel time to or from the medical center may involve as much as thirty minutes by car and considerably more by public transportation. This simple fact has conditioned some patients' choices; it is tedious to visit the Group (and to try to park one's car) and sometimes there is a long and anxious wait at home for the Group physician to answer a house-call. The outside services used are typically organized on a more local basis. The spatter of entrepreneurial practitioners throughout the neighborhoods of the area makes it easier for the patient to visit the doctor and for him to make house-calls promptly.

Somewhat more complicated than the ecological organization of practice is the way differences in administrative organization affect the temporal accessibility of services. The Montefiore Medical Group and the Family Health Maintenance Demonstration are so organized that the maximum number of services is offered to the maximum number of patients at minimum cost of physician time, without compromising the quality of care.[1] This rationalization of services is made possible not only by the large number of patients served, but also by the fact that with service contracts between patients and the practice the number of patients to be served is precisely calculable.

Efficiency requires elimination of as much waste as possible. For medical practice, waste is reduced primarily by maximizing the practitioner's caseload and minimizing the average time assigned to the patient. Given contractually committed patients, the number who must be served is known and the volume of

---

[1] See the discussion of this by Joseph Axelrod in "Administrative Aspects of Prepaid Medical Group Practice," unpublished M.S. thesis, School of Public Health, Yale University School of Medicine, 1951, pp. 37–38.

demand consequently predictable. This allows rather precise estimates of the number of physician-hours required and thus the number of physicians who must be available. Waste is eliminated by keeping the physicians continuously busy during their hours on duty. Advance appointments are stressed, since time assigned to emergencies and patients who just drop in is not easily predictable. Given minimal "open" professional time, the patient's claim of "emergency" is likely to be scrutinized rather closely before honoring it. The patient seeking help may thus not count on immediate service if he is not able to demonstrate severe need. Indeed, owing to the deliberately full caseload, unless his case is "special" he cannot count on being able to drop in or on getting an early appointment at an hour convenient to him.

The same rationalization lays its mark on house-calls. Rather than all physicians of the Medical Group being available every night, there is a system of rotation whereby physicians take turns being "on duty." The system contributes to efficiency because there is rarely as much demand for house-calls as for office-consultation; much time would be wasted if every physician were always on call. The system means, however, that the physician who is on duty is likely to be kept continuously busy—to have a list of households at which to call. Therefore, he must establish a system of priority to determine where to go first, which call is urgent and which can wait. In his attempt to determine the seriousness of the problem in advance, on the telephone, conflict develops between him and many patients who call.

The Family Health Maintenance Demonstration operated within this rationalized framework of services, but on a somewhat less strenuous schedule. The physician, with fewer than 150 families on his panel, had less work to do than the ordinary Montefiore Medical Group physician and relatively more time in which to do it. His patients were able to get more immediate appointments, even drop in unexpectedly and see the doctor after a short wait. The physician could be both liberal and prompt in making house-calls during the day. As we noted, the patients responded to this convenience with gratitude and enthusiasm. However, since the Demonstration physician did not make night-calls—the Medical Group physicians on duty were responsible for covering them—his patients had the same problems with night house-calls as other Medical Group patients had. This explains some of the outside utilization on the part of Demonstration patients.

Solo practice seems to consist typically in the adjustment of rather poorly defined professional resources to an essentially vague universe of patients.[1] Professional resources are poorly defined because the solo practitioner can never be sure how much time he must spend with patients on a given day. Beyond appointments, which are known in advance, there is also an unpredictable number of "walk-ins," emergency day calls, and night house-calls. By restricting practice to appointed consultations only and by refusing to make house-calls, as some specialists do, this indeterminacy can be reduced considerably; but so long as practice is organized individually, with patients entitled to make claims on an individual physician, it seems inevitable that there will be ambiguity in defining professional resources. The solo physician's time is never fully his own. Unless he gets some other physician to "cover" for him, or is engaged in a specialty that is not subject to emergency call, he puts in professional time while he sleeps; for his sleep may have to be interrupted to answer a call. The Group physician's sleep is his own personal time, for someone is "covering" his patients.

We can also infer another important aspect of solo practice— the indeterminate caseload. The inference is based upon the absence of such a formal contractual arrangement as occurs in HIP. When are those who have once consulted a solo physician his patients, and when not? How many of those who consult him are transients and how many are regulars on whom he can count? How many "regulars" will he see several times a year and how many once every few years? How many have just moved into

---

[1] Solo practice was not studied; therefore, much of what is said about it here is based on inference. In the present case, for example, if a patient states that he can get a solo physician any hour of the day or night, and if there is no reason to think he is exaggerating, we may presume that such a physician is not always busy and so can maintain an "open" practice.

the neighborhood and how many have moved out? Lacking a contract, there is bound to be ambiguity. Surely we may not believe that everyone named in the solo physician's files is still his patient. Some who have visited him will never again return, and it is quite uncertain who and how many they are. Thus, the number of people who call a solo practitioner for appointments on any single day, and the number of those who call for emergency treatment, or a house-call, cannot be predicted with security because the limits of the patient population are unknown. The indeterminacy of the patient population in a solo fee-for-service practice requires that the physician be always potentially available. To do otherwise than remain potentially available at all times requires a strong competitive position that some practitioners in The Bronx apparently lack.

The indeterminacy of the task posed by the fluidity of the patient population from day to day, the indeterminacy of the time that may be allocated to it, and the individual nature of entrepreneurial practice in combination constitute an organization of work that is "open" in character, whose demands on the practitioner are difficult to limit and rationalize. It is likely to be "closed" or limited when the physician has little fear of losing his patients—when he is sufficiently successful to remain attractive to the "right" patients in spite of relative inaccessibility, when the demand for his services is undiscourageable, when potential competitors are so few that he has a virtual monopoly, or when he is able to discriminate between "his" patients and strangers or "other" patients. But by the nature of the case, solo practice as such is *capable* of being fully open. Where it is open, it is available to the patient on a relatively flexible basis and so is likely to accommodate spur-of-the-moment calls or home visits. Its open character is facilitated by its decentralization.

What proportion of solo practices, like the legendary family doctor, is organized as an entirely open system is at present unknown. From surveys already cited in which the inaccessibility of physicians is deplored by a fairly large proportion of the public, we might suspect that many entrepreneurial practices are closed. It is the patient's experience with closed solo practices in

The Bronx that supports his frequent statement that "HIP is no worse than private practice." We need only recall the upper-lower-class woman who became annoyed because she had difficulty getting house-calls from the Montefiore Medical Group and consulted an "outside" pediatrician, only to find that he, too, was reluctant to make night house-calls; and returned resignedly to utilization of the Medical Group. Whatever the proportion, however, we know that *some* solo practices in The Bronx are "open." Five of the families interviewed had formed a regular relationship with a neighborhood physician solely for the purpose of using him for night house-call "emergencies." During the day they made regular use of the Montefiore Medical Group, but at night, when their "own" Group physician might not be on call and when they believed they were required to have a high temperature before the physician on duty would come, they used their neighborhood physician. They praised him for his willingness to visit them quickly and at any hour of the night, not for his skill as a doctor.

Such doctors do not grow on trees—even the plane trees of The Bronx. To have them the patient must find them. From what we have learned about the contrasting lay referral systems of our patients, we might infer that the upper-middle class patient has less difficulty finding such doctors—he tends to have had more experience with solo practitioners and is thus more likely to have consulted one with an open practice before he joined HIP. Even if his experience is slight, he can count on the informed and experienced referrals of his peers. And when available entrepreneurial practices are not open, he is more likely to be able to obtain special privileges by virtue of his social relations with the physician. In several interviews, instances were reported in which the physician was a relative or a close friend, and came some distance in the middle of the night to examine the patient as a personal favor.

Social class notwithstanding, we might say that patients who had a regular doctor before joining HIP, or those whose lay consultants have had wide experience with solo practitioners, or who have physicians as friends or relatives are likely to have access to solo practices that accommodate their demands, and are likely to go outside on occasion for reasons of convenience. Not all three of these inferences can be tested, but as we see in Table 16, more of those who had a regular doctor before joining HIP used outside medical services for convenience than did those who had no regular doctor before joining. By the nature of its organization, the Medical Group cannot be more convenient than open solo practices. Where convenience is the issue, where an alternative open practice is accessible, and where economic barriers are unimportant, there will be outside utilization of medical services.

TABLE 16. REASONS FOR USING OUTSIDE SERVICES AND HAVING A REGULAR DOCTOR BEFORE JOINING HIP

| Reasons for using outside services | Had regular doctor before joining HIP | Had no regular doctor before joining HIP |
|---|---|---|
| | Per cent | |
| Familiarity with outside doctor | 13 | 15 |
| Dissatisfaction with HIP | 46 | 61 |
| Accessibility of outside doctor | 41 | 24 |
| N | (218) | (59) |

$X^2 = 5.64$, $p < .10$. Combining rows 1 and 2, $X^2 = 5.52$, $p < .05$

## Reputation and Lay Referrals

One-third of all reasons given by the Montefiore Medical Group subscribers for the use of outside nonsurgical, nonobstetrical services concern the accessibility of the Medical Group. However, about one-half refer to some dissatisfaction with the services of the Medical Group, as does a somewhat smaller proportion of all reasons given for the use of outside surgical and obstetrical services. In such instances the patients' expectations have been violated. While we could postulate a relatively simple ecological and organizational logic surrounding the perceived accessibility or convenience of services, that logic does not seem appropriate for analysis of dissatisfaction. In the former case, we could reasonably assume that the way the patient looks at the doctor as an individual is a constant, the accessibility of his practice and the patient's desire for quick or convenient services are variables. In the latter case, it is precisely the patient's view of the doctor as an individual and the quality of the services he gives that is critical. In this there are a number of variables, from the element of anxiety to the element of organization.

When outside services were used before trying Montefiore Medical Group services, as in the case of those who were reluctant to leave their "old" doctor, the patients presumed that outside services were at least as good as those offered by the Medical Group. When the use of outside services followed specific complaints, such as poor or incorrect treatment or "lack of interest," the patients presumed that the outside physicians were *better* than those they had had in the Medical Group. The question is, How does the patient come to the conclusion that outside practitioners are as good or better than those of the Group, and what sustains it? The answer lies (1) in the personal experience of the patient, (2) in the reputation of the practice especially as it is affected by the lay referral system, and (3) in the organization of the practice.

Consider the use of outside services *before* the patient has even tried to use the Medical Group. Here the patient's choice is between remaining with a familiar physician and leaving him to use unfamiliar physicians for whose services he will pay no matter what the choice. In ordinary circumstances it is hard to imagine much of a problem choosing—insofar as the circumstances are routine, no pressing question of competence or technical facilities arises, and the extra fees are few. A preference for women doctors, timidity in the face of the unfamiliar service, or personal liking for the familiar doctor can tip the scales of choice. Where no particularly severe consequences seem likely to occur, individual whim and preference may have full play.

But when the circumstance of choice is one in which a crisis is perceived, we cannot assert mere whim in the choice between a familiar solo practitioner and an unfamiliar group practitioner. First of all, there is quite likely to be an emotional component weighting the patient's choice of a familiar practitioner in a moment of crisis. There is also an empirical, quasi-rational weight in the balance, for the fact that the familiar obstetrician's prior delivery of a baby was successful augurs well for his next delivery being successful. The unfamiliar Group obstetrician has had no such reassuring prior success with the new subscriber.

Why could the patient not have *heard* of the prior successes of the Group obstetrician with other deliveries? The answer is crucial: the Medical Group stands outside many lay referral systems in The Bronx. Reassuring familiarity is not only experiential in character but also reputational. The lay referral is the first source of knowledge about a doctor; personal experience follows. The reputation of the doctor tends to be a prior condition both for choice and for acquisition of personal experience with, and personal evaluation of, a physician. The social worker in the Family Health Maintenance Demonstration and the Medical Group doctor in The Bronx share the same faulty relation to the lay referral system—both are isolated.

Remembering that it is the extended family which tends to be the first level of lay consultation outside the household, we may observe that 80 per cent of the Demonstration patients responding indicated that they had no relatives who were subscribers to the Montefiore Medical Group. And even though it is workplace that is the major formal condition for HIP membership, the residence of the Demonstration patients' fellow-workers (and thus the particular HIP medical group to which fellow-workers belong) seems to vary so much that 49 per cent of those responding knew of no one at his place of work who also belonged to the Montefiore Medical Group. Indeed, given the turnover of physicians in the Medical Group itself, there is a fair chance that even lay consultants who are also members of the Medical Group will not be able to discuss the reputation of a particular Group physician, for the physician with whom the lay consultant is familiar may leave the Group and his place may be filled by a new and unknown physician. This means that if the Medical Group subscriber seeking testimony about the qualities of the physicians available to him in the Medical Group should consult his relatives, his neighbors, or his fellow-workers, they would not be likely to know anything about the Group, and even if they did, they would not be likely to know anything about the particular physician available to the questioner. It is considerably more likely that the subscriber's lay consultants could testify to the excellence of a neighborhood physician outside the Medical Group.

Entrepreneurial practice, which tends to limit its clientele to a smaller local circle in the first place, seems to be much better integrated into the reputation-sustaining lay referral systems. Its neighborhood location and its embodiment in a single long-term individual person help considerably to advance integration. And insofar as no formally selective contract arrangement is involved in entrepreneurial practice, its patients can be self-selected. Patients seem to select a practitioner not only on the basis of residential accessibility; their stimulation of each other is an important factor. If one is asked who is a good doctor, he is likely to name his own doctor, or a doctor he has had occasion to use or at least has heard of. The result is that the clientele of a neighborhood practice is composed of a number of small networks of patients who interact with each other in their response to their doctor. Such networks of lay influence are less likely to exist in the Medical Group practice.

Furthermore, unlike entrepreneurial practice, the Medical Group is identified with the legal-contractual system in which it is embedded. The Montefiore Medical Group is connected with the Health Insurance Plan of Greater New York and is so identified. However, there circulates among subscribers and potential subscribers a great deal of largely critical gossip about the Health Insurance Plan. Of the patients interviewed only four could recall hearing any enthusiasm or praise expressed for the Health Insurance Plan (though a considerable number of those interviewed themselves expressed enthusiasm). The Health Insurance Plan, as a fairly recent and contentious innovation in New York, is rather conspicuous and stands distinct from the loose organization of entrepreneurial practice. So while the unsatisfactory behavior of one solo practitioner rarely is taken by the outraged patient as a reflection on the system of "private practice," the patient frequently seems to regard the unsatisfactory behavior of one HIP physician as a reflection on HIP itself. Several patients told of people they knew who, believing that a HIP doctor had made a mistake or that they had been insulted by a HIP doctor, canceled their contracts with HIP.[1] In this sense, then, patients of the Medical Group are unlikely to be acquainted with anyone who knows anything about particular doctors of their group but they are quite likely to have heard some highly negative gossip about HIP or HIP doctors in general. The situation is somewhat tempered by fact that individual HIP medical groups have their own individual reputations.[2] A number of the patients interviewed had transferred to the Montefiore Medical Group not because they had heard of a particular physician in it, but because they had heard that the Group was a good one. Indeed, only two patients recalled hearing gossip that was highly critical of the Medical Group as opposed to HIP in general.

### Reputation and Professional Referrals

By the nature of its organization the Medical Group tends to be isolated from the lay referral system. Insofar as preoccupation with the reputation of a physician is a factor in choosing him—and we must recall that this is not often the case among the patients studied—it is more likely to send the patient outside for medical service than to the Montefiore Medical Group. An additional aspect of the way the organization of the Medical Group is faultily integrated into the lay referral system is shown when we consider occasions in which the patient goes outside the Group to seek an independent opinion about a diagnosis or prescription, or to seek a different sort of treatment. Why don't those patients seek opinions *within* the Medical Group? Part of the answer may lie in the Group physicians' discouragement of such, though there is no evidence of this in the interviews. A more important answer lies in the fact that such patients cannot conceive of the possibility of independent opinions among physicians of the

[1] We might mention again here that by the nature of this study such people were not interviewed. The sample that was interviewed is obviously limited in character.

[2] Rothenberg and others have the same impression. See Rothenberg, Robert E., Karl Pickard, and Joel E. Rothenberg, *Group Medicine and Health Insurance in Action*, Crown Publishers, New York, 1949, p. 122.

Medical Group. As one patient said rather truculently when asked why he did not consider a Medical Group surgeon to be an independent source of corroboration of a Medical Group internist's opinion, "They work together, don't they? They're bound to back each other up." Those with whom Group physicians do not appear to work—physicians outside the Medical Group—are the source of independent opinion. The Medical Group is seen by the patients to be a professionally closed referral system.

This is reflected in instances where the patient is apprehensive about his illness—its diagnosis, treatment, or prescription—and entertains some doubts about the Group physician under whose care he is or will be. If he does happen to know someone who can testify to the physician's qualities, his response is quick and direct. A husband's anxiety was allayed after he learned from his supervisor that the Medical Group surgeon who was to operate on his wife had already operated successfully on the supervisor's wife. A pregnant lower-middle class woman sought outside obstetrical service after she chatted in the Medical Group waiting-room with another pregnant woman and heard frightening things about her Medical Group obstetrician.[1] But when there is no corroboration of the physician's virtues some patients either procrastinate or seek outside medical service. For example, one lower-middle class mother received with anxiety the recommendation that her daughter undergo minor surgery. She asked the Medical Group pediatrician who made the recommendation how she could tell whether the surgeon was "any good" or not. The pediatrician, she reported, answered that the success of the operation would determine that. Isolated from her kin, with few friends and very little experience with doctors, she had no one outside to turn to; and she procrastinated.

Referrals within the professional system of the Medical Group, then, can be seen by uncertain patients to be a function of the

[1] "Particularly dangerous are conversations at the polyclinic while awaiting their turn. We are reminded here of the sensible idea of some doctors of putting in their waiting-rooms a notice: 'Please do not discuss your complaints with each other.' " Pondoev, G. S., *Notes of a Soviet Doctor*. Consultants Bureau, Inc., New York, 1959, p. 80.

professionally closed organization of the Group rather than the free judgment of the professional workers involved. A patient or an outside doctor can testify persuasively to the Group physician's skill, not another Group physician. And only an outside doctor may give independent corroboration of the Group physician's opinion, not another Group physician.

In contrast, patients who provided data on entrepreneurial physicians seemed to think that their actions were independent, lacking any regular commitment to a definite circle of colleagues. Only one patient made any reference at all to suspicion of fee-splitting and other less venal and more common marks of the entrepreneurial physician's participation in a limited (which is to say closed) professional referral network.[1] When referred by a neighborhood practitioner to "the best man in the city," there was no doubt expressed by the patient that the consultant was not "the best man." It is, of course, possible in the relatively open system of solo practice that one can be referred to the worst man in the city as well as the best. To the patient, however, there is no practical limit on the quality of referrals made by an entrepreneurial practitioner;[2] in the Medical Group he sees that he must be referred only to those who participate in the organization.

## The Weight of Professional Opinion

Both its rationalization of professional time and its removal of professional referrals and reputations from lay hands constitute part of a more general characteristic of the Medical Group:

[1] On colleague relations in solo practice, see the papers of Oswald Hall, listed in footnote on p. 32.

[2] There was some indication from Family Health Maintenance Demonstration patients that nonphysician personnel could serve this function of giving "independent" testimonial to the ability of a Group physician or to the excellence of his opinion. These personnel—secretaries, social workers, and nurses—seemed on some occasions reported by patients to be able to lay doubts to rest when physicians could not. With respect to the quality of a specialist, this "independent" testimonial discouraged more than one patient's inclination to go outside—at least when it appeared spontaneous and informal rather than a direct "professional" answer to a question about whether Doctor X was "any good" or not. And with respect to medical opinion, several cases were recorded in which patients did not think the physician's recommendations were correct and did not follow them until they happened to get the same recommendation from the public health nurse in what appeared to them to be an independent context.

comparatively thorough imposition of organized professional controls on practice. The HIP Medical Control Board determines who is qualified to practice a speciality. A professional committee determines the "proper" caseload for the practicing Group physician. Specialists may not be used by the patient without medical referral. The physician's cases are subject to review by a committee of colleagues, and his medical records are subject to evaluation and inspection by a visiting Medical Care Studies Committee. Not only are his patients' demands for immediate consultation countered by administrative policies that make for full appointment books, then, but his patients' demands for, let us say, penicillin, are countered by colleague emphasis on conservative use of antibiotics.

Professional control in the Medical Group seems to solidify the difference between lay and professional perspectives, and thus increase or intensify conflict. Inevitably occasions arise when the patients want service more quickly than can be provided or under circumstances which the physician considers unnecessary. The patient thinks, "My temperature of 99.7° may not be high, but it may be the beginning of something serious and I want to be looked at right away just to make sure," whereas the physician thinks, "He probably has a simple URI [upper-respiratory infection] and can wait or come in tomorrow; meanwhile I can attend to a cardiac case or a spontaneous abortion." In a system in which professional time is maximized the patient cannot get service on demand. He gets service on the basis of the professional's assessment of the importance of his demand. This is built into the system, and some patient disaffection is inevitable.

The same is true for the considerably more complicated matter of diagnosis and treatment. Continuing our earlier example, the patient "knows" that penicillin is good for his bronchitis. He remembers that an earlier attack cleared up quickly when his former doctor treated him with penicillin. The Group physician, however, has attended clinical conferences at which the growing literature on secondary diseases attributed to antibiotics was discussed and recalls the comments on the use of medication by the last visiting committee reviewing medical records: he recommends to the patient treatment that is more professionally acceptable than massive doses of penicillin. The patient may insist, he may complain; but the physician is strongly motivated to be firm.

The definiteness and security of professional opinion is by no means so well shaped in solo practice. The entrepreneurial physician is not necessarily in regular interaction with his colleagues. Without colleague interaction he lacks a major source of new information,[1] and perhaps more importantly, lacks a potent source of reinforcement of the information he already has. He is therefore in a comparatively poor position to resist his patients' demands, particularly if his practice is so insecure that he is afraid of losing his patients. Even if he does not lack all the up-to-date information on the dangers of antibiotics, the fact that he may be cut off from the continuous reinforcement of that information by his colleagues may, in the face of continuous patient requests, lead him to decide that the patient's desire for penicillin is either reasonable or at least harmless enough to humor.

Thus, the patient is less likely to find Medical Group practitioners willing to accept or tolerate his lay opinions about diagnosis and treatment, and so may take occasion to go outside to find a more tolerant practitioner. However, one possible counterbalance to the weight of professional opinion in the Medical Group is its bureaucratic context. The Medical Group patient may generate considerable pressure by insisting on the letter of his contractual rights and, if disgruntled, he may complain to both the director of the Medical Group and the proper official of the Health Insurance Plan. Medical Group physicians are, in fact, exceedingly sensitive to "demanding" patients, and sometimes feel quite oppressed by them.

---

[1] For a study of the adoption of a new drug by some doctors, in which it was found that the physician isolated from his colleagues tended to rely upon commercial sources for his information, see Menzel, Herbert, and Elihu Katz, "Social Relations and Innovation in the Medical Profession: The Epidemiology of a New Drug" in *Patients, Physicians, and Illness,* edited by E. Gartly Jaco, The Free Press, Glencoe, Ill., 1958, pp. 517–528. The study, soon to be reported at greater length, emphasizes the significance of colleague relations to receiving and making use of new medical information.

A stark example of the way a patient can press for her "rights" is provided by an atypical case:

While enrolled in HIP a married woman had bloody stools. After bleeding persisted she made repeated visits to her Family Doctor, fearing cancer. She reported that the doctor said she just had piles and he discouraged her efforts to obtain a referral to a specialist. She telephoned to the downtown administrative office of HIP and insisted on her right to see a specialist. The central office suggested, she reported, that she transfer to the Montefiore Medical Group. Upon transfer, she was given a proctoscopy, with apparently negative findings. Dissatisfied, she asked for a hemorrhoidectomy, but her Family Doctor said that it would not do much good inasmuch as the difficulty would recur. She again asked for and obtained a proctoscopy, however, and at the time of the interview was asking for another.

When she was pregnant she chose "the best obstetrician in the Group." At about eight months of term she began to have labor pains and called her obstetrician. He instructed her husband to check on the frequency of the contractions, and when he reported them as coming close together the obstetrician told the couple to take a taxi to the hospital. They asked that he send an ambulance since they were entitled to one. The physician, reported the wife, again suggested a taxi and hung up the receiver. After a brief conference with his wife, the husband called back and demanded that the physician order an ambulance because his HIP contract covered that service. The ambulance was ordered and the wife was delivered of her baby in the hospital.

The wife reported that it was her practice to exaggerate her symptoms over the telephone in order to make sure that she would get a house-call when she wanted one. And she consciously holds as a reserve weapon the threat to call "headquarters" and complain about the treatment she gets. *Caveat venditor!*

In entrepreneurial practice, patient pressures must perforce be considerably different in nature. Without a contract, the patient has no clearly defined "rights," and without a bureaucratic structure, no clear channels through which he can go to express his grievances. Short of "dropping" the doctor, which, of course, does not redress a grievance, or instituting a lawsuit, which is not easy, the patient's pressure must be rather covert and difficult for the doctor to be fully aware of. In the Medical Group they are likely to be more directly expressed by the patient and so more directly perceived by the physician. Aside from their great annoyance value, however, they are likely to be effective in the Medical Group only when directed toward concretely defined contract benefits. The patient can expect some success when he insists on his "right" to an ambulance, a proctoscopy, a house-call, or an examination by a specialist, even when his Family Doctor disapproves; his contract states that he is entitled to such service if he needs it, and until it is provided no one can know whether he "really" needs it or not. On the other hand, his contract does not specify his right to a prescription of penicillin or a hemorrhoidectomy. Thus, in spite of definite channels for patient pressure, medical opinion in the Medical Group is heavily insulated from lay opinion. Compared to an insecure or professionally isolated solo practice, the patient is likely to find few of his prejudices honored in the Medical Group.

# PART THREE

# IMAGES FOR THE STUDY OF MEDICAL CARE

# 9. Dilemmas in the Doctor-Patient Relationship

IN PART TWO OF THIS BOOK we were concerned with instances in which patients evaded the expectations of the professionals who were caring for them. In the Family Health Maintenance Demonstration many patients would not accept the services of the social worker in spite of their need and the recommendation of the physician and nurse. In the Montefiore Hospital Medical Group a sizable proportion of patients chose to avoid services to which they were entitled by contract. A lesser but nonetheless important proportion of Demonstration patients used outside services even when they were enrolled in a program with which they expressed overwhelming general satisfaction. Analysis indicated that the patient rejected professional services when they did not fit into his scheme of things—when they were isolated from the steps he goes through in seeking help, when they contradicted his own and his lay consultants' conception of illness and treatment, when they were insulated from the way by which he and his lay consultants try to establish their reliability, and when they required him to sacrifice personal convenience. The professional expects patients to accept what he recommends on his terms; patients seek services on their own terms. In that each seeks to gain his own terms, there is conflict.

How typical of the doctor-patient relationship is conflict? The profession itself contends, as Hughes observed, "that there is no conflict of interest or perspective between professional and client —or at least . . . none between the good professional and the good client."[1] It may be that the professionals of the Demonstra-

[1] Hughes, Everett C., "The Sociological Study of Work: An Editorial Foreword," *American Journal of Sociology*, vol. 57, March, 1952, p. 425.

tion and the Medical Group are not all they should be, but they all have excellent credentials and those observed at work seemed to possess admirable skill and conscientiousness. It may also be that patients in The Bronx are unusually demanding and arrogant, but, except for one or two, those interviewed seemed to have only the best of intentions. It is quite likely that the particular situation studied stimulated more overt conflict than is present in other situations, but the nature of the conflict itself did not seem unusual.

## The Ageless Struggle

Struggle between patient and doctor seems to have gone on throughout recorded history. Almost 2500 years ago, the Hippocratic corpus collected doctors' complaints about the nonprofessional criteria that people used to select their physicians,[1] criticism of patients for insisting on "out of the way and doubtful remedies"[2] or on overconventional remedies like "barley water, wine and hydromel,"[3] and for disobeying the doctor's orders.[4]

The patients who have left us documents often treat the physician as a potential danger to which one must respond cautiously and whom one must always be ready to evade. Patients have circulated stories about the occasions on which they successfully cured themselves, or continued to live for a long time in defiance of medical prognoses. This sort of literature may be represented by the Roman "epigram about a doctor Marcus who touched a statue of Zeus, and although Zeus was made of stone he nevertheless died,"[5] and by Benvenuto Cellini's little story:

> I put myself once more under doctor's orders, and attended to their directions, but grew worse. When fever fell upon me, I resolved on having recourse again to the wood: but the doctors forbade it, saying that if I took it with the fever on me, I should not have a week to

[1] *Hippocrates.* Translated and edited by W. H. S. Jones. William Heinemann, London, 1943, vol. 2, pp. 67, 281, 311.

[2] *Ibid.*, vol. 1, p. 317.

[3] *Ibid.*, vol. 2, p. 67.

[4] *Ibid.*, vol. 2, pp. 201, 297.

[5] Pondoev, G. S., *Notes of a Soviet Doctor.* Consultants Bureau, Inc., New York, 1959, p. 87.

live. However, I made my mind up to disobey their orders, observed the same diet as I had formerly adopted, and after drinking the decoction four days, was wholly rid of fever. . . . After fifty days my health was re-established.[1]

Physicians have left us instructive essays on "decorum"— practical guides to the physician for managing his relations with the patient in such a way that threats to his authority are minimized. An example that, by anticipating patient resistance, reveals much about the physician's problems is the wise and devious advice of a writer of the school of Salerno:

At your entrance inquire of him who greets you from what disease the sick man suffers and how his illness progresses; this is advisable in order that when you come to him you may not seem entirely uninformed as to the illness. . . . Again when you reach the house and before you see him, ask if he has seen his confessor, and if he has not done this, arrange for him to do so, or have him promise to do so, because if the sick man hears talk on this subject after he has been examined, and the signs of his illness studied, he will begin to despair of his safety, because he will think that you despair of it. Entering the sick-room you should have neither proud nor greedy countenance; you should repeat the greeting of those who rise as you enter, and with a gesture seat yourself when they sit down. Next you may resume the conversation with a few remarks in which you praise the neighborhood, commend the arrangements of the house, if it seems appropriate, or compliment the liberality of the family.

Then turning to the patient you may ask how it goes with him, and have him put out his arm. At first there may be differences between your own state and that of the patient, either because he is excited at your arrival, or because he is worried about the size of your fee, so that you find the pulse rather confusing; therefore you should consider the pulse only after the patient has become steadier. Take care that he does not lie upon his side nor has his finger overextended or flexed against his palm. Support his arm with your left hand and observe the pulse for at least 100 beats in order to feel all its variations, and thus you will be able to satisfy the expectant bystanders with words which they are glad to hear.

Next have the urine brought to you that the sick man may see you study his illnesses not only from the pulse but from the urine. When

[1] *The Autobiography of Benvenuto Cellini.* Translated by J. A. Symonds. Modern Library, New York, n.d., p. 128.

examining the urine you should observe its color, substance, quantity, and content; after which you may promise the patient that with the help of God you will cure him. As you go away, however, you should say to his servants that he is in a very bad way, because if he recovers you will receive great credit and praise, and if he dies, they will remember that you despaired of his health from the beginning. Meanwhile, I urge you not to turn a lingering eye upon his wife, his daughter, or his maid-servant, for this sort of thing blinds the eye of the doctor, averts the favor of God, and makes the doctor abhorrent to the patient and less confident in himself. Be therefore careful in speech, respectable in conduct, attentively seeking Divine aid. If the people of the house invite you to a meal, as often happens, do not seem too much gratified, and do not seek the first place at the table, although it is the custom to give this to the priest or the doctor. Do not criticize the food or drink, and when in the country do not show distaste for country food, for example, millet bread, even though you can scarcely control your stomach.[1]

Struggle between physician and patient has not been restricted to times past. The contemporary studies recorded in Paul's volume, the work of Saunders, Clark, Koos, and many others reveal that elsewhere, as in The Bronx, patients do not always do what physicians tell them to do. They persist in diagnosing and dosing themselves and in assigning great weight to lay advice and their own personal dispositions. It is difficult to get them to cooperate wholly with health programs that, professionals believe, are for their own good.[2]

That the problem continues is somewhat paradoxical, for it seems unquestionable that the medical practitioner has reached an all-time peak of prestige and authority in the eyes of the public. The physician of today is an essentially new kind of professional whose scientific body of knowledge and occupational freedom are quite recent acquisitions. His knowledge is now far more precise and effective than it has ever been in the past, since for the first time it could be said that from " 'about the year

[1] Corner, George W., "The Rise of Medicine at Salerno in the Twelfth Century," *Annals of Medical History*, vol. 3, January, 1931, pp. 14–15. Quoted from pamphlet of anonymous Salernitan, "On the Visit of a Physician to His Patient," de Reni, ii: 74–75.

[2] Cobb, Sidney, Stanley King, and Edith Chen, "Differences Between Respondents and Nonrespondents in a Morbidity Survey Involving Clinical Examination," *Journal of Chronic Diseases*, vol. 6, August, 1957, pp. 95–108.

1910 or 1912 . . . [in the United States] a random patient with a random disease consulting a doctor chosen at random stood better than a 50-50 chance of benefiting from the encounter.' "[1] The physician has obtained unrivaled power to control his own practice and the affairs that impinge upon it, and the patient now has severely limited access to drugs for self-treatment and to nonmedical practitioners for alternative treatment. But the ancient problem continues.

## The Clash of Perspectives

It is my thesis that the separate worlds of experience and reference of the layman and the professional worker are always in potential conflict with each other.[2] This seems to be inherent in the very situation of professional practice. The practitioner, looking from his professional vantage point, preserves his detachment by seeing the patient as a case to which he applies the general rules and categories learned during his protracted professional training. The client, being personally involved in what happens, feels obliged to try to judge and control what is happening to him. Since he does not have the same perspective as the practitioner, he must judge what is being done from other than a professional point of view. While both professional worker and client are theoretically in accord with the end of their relationship—solving the client's problems—the means by which this solution is to be accomplished and the definitions of the problem itself are sources of potential difference.[3] The very nature of professional practice seems to stimulate the patient on occasion to be

[1] Gregg, Alan, *Challenges to Contemporary Medicine.* Columbia University Press, New York, 1956, p. 13, quoting L. J. Henderson.

[2] Cf. Merton, Robert K., "The Role-Set: Problems in Sociological Theory," *British Journal of Sociology*, vol. 8, June, 1957, p. 112.

[3] "In many occupations the workers or practitioners . . . deal routinely with what are emergencies to the people who receive their services. This is a source of chronic tension between the two. For the person with the crisis feels that the other is trying to belittle his trouble; he does not take it seriously enough. His very competence comes from having dealt with a thousand cases of what the client likes to consider his unique trouble. The worker thinks he knows from long experience that people exaggerate their troubles. He therefore builds up devices to protect himself, to stall people off. . . . Involved in this is something of the struggle . . . to maintain some control over one's decision of what work to do, and over the disposition of one's time and of one's routine of life." Hughes, Everett C., *Men and Their Work.* The Free Press, Glencoe, Ill., 1958, pp. 54–55.

especially wary and questioning. Professional knowledge is never complete, and so diagnosis, made with the greatest of care and the best of contemporary skill, may turn out to be inappropriate for any particular case. These mistakes[1] may occur in two basic ways.

First of all, it is obvious that in every age including our own, there are likely to be worthless diagnostic categories and associated treatments—sometimes merely harmless without contributing anything to cure, sometimes downright dangerous. As Shryock put it for an earlier time, "No one will ever know just what impact heroic practice [heavy bleeding and dosing with calomel] had on American vital statistics: therapy was never listed among the causes of death."[2] In addition, in every age there are likely to be diseases unrecognized by contemporary diagnostic categories—as typhoid and typhus were not distinguished before 1820, as gonorrhea and syphilis were once confused, and as mental diseases are no doubt being confused today. Thus, the best contemporary knowledge may on occasion be misdirected or false, and some of the patient's complaints wrongfully ignored.

Second, however, is a considerably more complex source of error that flows not from knowledge so much as from the enterprise of applying knowledge to everyday life. Insofar as knowledge consists in general and objective diagnostic categories by which the physician sorts the concrete signs and complaints confronting him, it follows that work assumes a routine character. The routine classifies the flow of reality into a limited number of categories so that the individual items of that flow become reduced to mere instances of a class, each individual instance being considered the same as every other in its class.

The routine of practice not only makes varied elements of experience equivalent—it also makes them *ordinary*. In general medical practice, while the range of complaints may indeed be unusually wide, the number of complaints falling within a rather

---

[1] See "Mistakes at Work," *ibid.*, pp. 88–101.

[2] Shryock, Richard H., *Medicine and Society in America, 1660–1860*. New York University Press, New York, 1960, p. 111.

narrow range seems to be overwhelming. In our day, for example, complaints that are categorized as upper-respiratory infections are exceedingly common. Like malaria in the nineteenth
century, they are so common that they are considered ordinary.
And insofar as they are considered ordinary it is not legitimate
for the patient to make a great fuss about the suffering they
involve. His subjectively real pain is given little attention or
sympathy because it is too ordinary to worry about. His response
to this may be gauged by reading Dr. Raffel's self-pitying account
of the reception of his complaint of acute sinusitis.[1]

What also happens is that more of reality than proves to be
appropriate tends to be subsumed under the ordinary and commonly used categories. This again seems to be in the very nature
of professional practice—if *most* patients have upper-respiratory
infections when they complain of sneezing, sounds in the head,
a running nose and fatigue, then an upper-respiratory infection is
probably involved when *one* particular person makes the complaint. It could, indeed, be an allergy or even approaching deafness,[2] but it is not probable—that is to say, it was not commonly
the case in the past. The physician cannot do otherwise than
make such assumptions, but by the statistical nature of the case
he cannot help being wrong sometimes.

### The Patient's Problem

These problems of diagnosis are not only problems for the
doctor but for the patient as well. All the patient knows is what
he feels and what he has heard. He feels terrible, his doctor tells
him that there's nothing to worry about, and a friend tells him
about someone who felt the same way and dropped dead as he
was leaving the consulting-room with a clean bill of health. For
the patient the problem is, When are subjective sensations so
reliable that one should insist on special attention, and when can
one reasonably allow them to be waved away as tangential,
ordinary and unimportant; when is the doctor mistaken? The

[1] In *When Doctors Are Patients*, edited by Max Pinner and B. F. Miller. W. W.
Norton and Co., New York, 1952, pp. 236-241.

[2] Dr. Max Samter's physician had diagnosed a cold and prescribed nose drops
and epsom salts before deafness overtook him. *Ibid.*, pp. 62-72.

answer to these questions is never definite for any individual case, and indeed cannot be resolved decisively except by subsequent events. All of us know of events that have contradicted the judgment of the physician, and, of course, many others that have contradicted the patient.

The situation of consultation thus proves to involve ambiguities that provide grounds for doubt by the patient. Furthermore, those ambiguities are objective. Most reasonable people will agree that the doctor is sometimes wrong, whether by virtue of overlooking the signs that convert an ordinary-appearing case into a special case, or by virtue of the deficiencies of the knowledge of his time. He is less often wrong now than he was a hundred years ago, but frequency is not really the question for the individual. Even if failure occurs once in ten thousand cases, the question for the patient is whether it is he who is to be that one case, a question that no one can answer in advance. If the evidence of his senses and the evidence of his knowledge and that of his intimate consultants are contradicted by the physician, the patient may understandably feel it prudent to seek another physician or to evade the prescriptions he has already obtained.

### The Role of Ignorance in Doctor-Patient Conflict

It has been rightly assumed by many writers that much of the conflict between doctor and patient is caused by the patient's misinformation, or ignorance. When the patient expects a good, sensible remedy like barley water, wine, and hydromel and is outraged by the doctor's insistence on a dietary regimen, when he expects penicillin and rejects aspirin, he is misinformed about the correct remedy. If he were properly educated, the argument goes, he would be equipped to expect from the doctor what the doctor wants to give him. Through "health education," a major source of conflict is supposed to be eliminated by teaching the patient to conform to the expectations of the doctor.[1]

There is, however, a dilemma in the relation of health education to doctor-patient conflict. One side of the dilemma appears

[1] Talcott Parsons in *The Social System* (The Free Press, Glencoe, Ill., 1951, p. 438) defines the patient's role by reference to the doctor's expectations.

when we ask what sort of conflict exists when the patient has no "health education" at all—that is to say, no culturally determined expectations of the doctor. Situations like this are found in veterinary and pediatric medicine—at least when the parent or owner of the patient does not take a surrogate sick role. Patients in both cases lack any health education. As such, they lack the knowledge that would lead them, when ill, to seek a physician. Unassisted, they are likely either to seek a familiar sympathetic person or, like the lion in the fable, lie helpless somewhere waiting for the chance and professionally unqualified kindness of an Androcles. If they should happen to strike upon a treatment situation, they prove incapable of indicating by any but the crudest and largely involuntary means—like a swollen paw and roars of distress—what it is that is wrong with them. Nor can they themselves be counted upon to follow or even to submit to the treatment prescribed. Indeed, it often happens that they must be physically restrained to be treated.

It is patent that there are shortcomings in working with patients having no health education at all, but are there any virtues? One is that while the patient may be incapable of illuminating his complaint because of his lack of education he is also incapable of obscuring it by the irrelevant and the misinformed, or compounding it by imaginative anticipation. Another is that he has no expectations about treatment, so that once the consultant establishes control there is no contradiction of his authority.[1] Another is that by the very reason that the patient cannot be expected to cooperate voluntarily it is permissible to use physical restraint, a very convenient device for practice that cannot be used on people who theoretically can but will not cooperate.[2] And finally, apocryphal but worth citing nonetheless,

[1] In this context must be cited a sophisticated essay that has not received the attention due it—Szasz, Thomas S., and M. H. Hollander, "A Contribution to the Philosophy of Medicine," *A. M. A. Archives of Internal Medicine*, vol. 97, 1956, pp. 585–592. See their treatment of the "activity-passivity" model of the doctor-patient relationship in the context of veterinary and pediatric medicine.

[2] In surgery, as Szasz and Hollander point out, people are legitimately restrained by anesthetic or by force. License to restrain or immobilize the patient makes the practice of surgery considerably less complicated than the practice of medicine, though the surgeon has the problem of getting the patient to agree to surgery in the first place.

the ignorant client, once won over, may, like Androcles' lion, show undying gratitude and devotion to his healer. If this is true, it is no mean virtue.

However, the virtues of the completely ignorant patient may seem small in the face of the shortcomings. After all, patients who are educated in health affairs will have the knowledge that enables them to recognize symptoms so as to consult a doctor in time, give a useful history, and cooperate intelligently with treatment. Surely, then, people with the most health education will be more cooperative and will not struggle with the doctor.

It does not seem to be so simple. The physician is the one with the greatest possible health education, but there are good grounds for believing that he is not a very cooperative patient. The physician is reputed to be given to a great deal of self-diagnosis and treatment. This follows in part from his advanced health education, which makes him feel competent to diagnose himself "scientifically," and in part, like his susceptibility to drug addiction, from his privileged access to the medication that his self-diagnosis calls for. And when, after the long delay caused by self-diagnosis and treatment, the physician does seek the aid of another, he is reputed to be an argumentative and uncooperative patient incapable of repressing his own opinions in favor of those of his consultant.[1] This too seems to follow from his very health education, for he has a "scientific" position on which to stand and counter that of his consultant, and a clear insight into the uncertainties of practice, so that he may feel strongly justified in holding to his own opinion.

This view of physicians as patients is made more credible when we recall the material already presented on the behavior of the well-educated patient in The Bronx. Fairly well versed in modern medicine, on occasion he cooperates admirably with the physician, but on occasion he is also quite active in evaluating the physician on the basis of his own knowledge and "shopping

[1] The bad reputation of the doctor as patient is not limited to the United States. Pondoev (*op. cit.*, pp. 104–105), observes, "If we ask any doctor he will agree with any other that the most difficult patient is a sick doctor. No other patient interferes so much with the doctor in his work as does the ailing doctor to make his case understood. . . . Nothing is more difficult than to convince the sick doctor that he is mistaken in his own diagnosis."

around" for diagnoses or prescriptions consonant with his knowledge. He is more confident and cooperative in routine situations, perhaps, but he is also more confident of his own ability to judge the physician and dispose himself accordingly. A less-educated patient may be far more manageable.[1]

The dilemma in patient education is now clear. When he lacks health education the prospective patient is unlikely to seek the aid of a professional consultant, and he is unable to give the doctor a history or cooperate with the treatment. When he is well educated the prospective patient is confident of his ability to treat himself "scientifically," and when he sees a doctor he feels more confident of his own ability to judge the doctor's services.[2]

## The Role of Confidence in Doctor-Patient Conflict

If it is true that the practice of medicine involves both contradiction of the patient's viewpoint and sufficient uncertainty that the patient may find good reasons for resisting the doctor's opinions, and if increasing the knowledge of the patient fails to persuade him to adjust to the doctor's viewpoint, perhaps the doctor's professional status may itself persuade the patient to cooperate. Some of the rather more breathless writers on medicine claim that a compelling aura of mystery and magical power surrounds the healer's role; analytically inclined writers discuss how, unlike the businessman with his motto *caveat emptor*, the special status of the professional grants him an *a priori* trust and confidence.[3]

[1] Wilbert E. Moore and Melvin M. Tumin in "Some Social Functions of Ignorance" (*American Sociological Review*, vol. 14, December, 1949, pp. 788–789) point out that the ignorance of the client is useful in that it preserves the privileged position of the specialist: when the client gains such special knowledge, he can dispense with the specialist.

[2] Howard S. Becker in "Social Class Variations in the Teacher-Pupil Relationship" (*Journal of Educational Sociology*, vol. 25, April, 1956, pp. 451–465) has observed the same dilemma for the schoolteacher: lower class pupils do not make any trouble, but also do not learn; middle class pupils learn, but their parents are always interfering in school affairs.

Rose Coser in "A Home Away from Home" (*Sociological Studies of Health and Sickness*, edited by Dorian Apple, McGraw-Hill Book Co., New York, pp. 168–169) notes that the passive patient facilitates treatment but resists recovery; the active patient interferes with treatment but is better equipped to drop the sick role and recover.

[3] Almost all writers on the professions assert this in one way or another. For a direct statement, see Gross, Edward, *Work and Society*, Thomas Y. Crowell Co., New York, 1958, p. 78.

The usual conception of confidence is shallow and parochial. It is indeed true as we saw in The Bronx that under ordinary circumstances one consults a doctor because he assumes that he knows his business and that his judgment may be trusted, but it is no less true of the use of other services. It is a mistake to assume that the title "profession" confers a kind of authority[1] on the practitioner which is greatly different from the authority of any specialist, professional or not. Simmel pointed out some time ago that

> . . . our modern life is based to a much larger extent than is usually realized upon the faith in the honesty of the other. . . . We base our gravest decisions on a complex system of conceptions, most of which presuppose the confidence that we will not be betrayed.[2]

Under normal circumstances we have confidence in a mechanic's ability to grease our car properly just as we have confidence in a physician's ability to prescribe the right drug for us and a pharmacist's ability to fill the prescription accurately. In the same fashion we have confidence in a variety of other service workers— appliance repairmen, bank clerks, carpenters, and fitting-room tailors. Faith in a consultant's honest application of his specialized ability seems to be connected not only with the use of those who are called professionals, but also with the use of any kind of consultant whose work is fairly esoteric. It must exist if life is to function smoothly, routinely.

However, there seems to be a generic distinction in the way the definition of the situation of consultation varies. On the one hand, there is a fundamentally superficial confidence that is automatically attached to any routine consultation. In The Bronx it was elicited by the M.D. degree and the license to practice, and enhanced by lay reputation. It was manifested in uncritical cooperation with the consultant. This sort of confidence

[1] Strictly speaking, the expert does not have the authority of office that "exacts obedience." His "authority" only exerts influence. See Bierstedt, Robert, "The Problem of Authority" in *Freedom and Control in Modern Society*, edited by Morroe Berger, Theodore Abel, and Charles E. Page, D. Van Nostrand Co., New York, 1954, pp. 67–81.

[2] *The Sociology of Georg Simmel*. Edited and translated by K. H. Wolff. The Free Press, Glencoe, Ill., 1950, p. 313.

sustains the doctor-patient relationship in about the same way it sustains any consultant-client relationship. In The Bronx questions arose when the consultant did not act as he was expected to, when the diagnosis seemed implausible, when the prescription seemed intolerable and unnecessary, and when "cure" was slow or imperceptible. They became pressing when the problem of consultation assumed what seemed to be serious proportions. What was needed to sustain the relationship was a stronger sort of confidence than supported initial consultation.

It may be that this stronger sort of confidence is in the minds of those who make a special connection between professions and client confidence. Certainly it is true that three of the old, established professions deal with some of the most anxiety-laden topics of existence—the body, the soul, human relations, and property. Anxiety inherent in those topics, a stronger confidence is required for entrusting oneself to doctors, clergymen, and lawyers than to plumbers, piano-tuners, and fitting-room tailors. However, we have enough evidence from The Bronx study to know that in the early stages of illness there is not enough anxiety even to motivate search for professional help. One first tries tinkering with his piano himself before deciding to call in a professional tuner; one first tries tinkering with his organs himself before calling in a doctor. In the later stages of illness, when anxiety does occur, it can as well interfere with as sustain confidence. Consultants with professional standing thus *claim* confidence, but do not necessarily get it.

## The Role of Irrationality in Doctor-Patient Conflict

Perhaps it is in the light of observing patient anxiety and the dysfunctional effects of patient education that it is argued that by the nature of the case the patient cannot exercise his reason. Indeed, it has been a persistent part of professional ideology to insist that no matter how knowledgeable he is, the patient is incapable of reliable judgment. The implication follows that he should therefore be relieved, like an infant or a lion, of the opportunity to judge a physician's work.

Both the strength and the weakness of professional deprecation of the patient's judgment is revealed with charming innocence in a passage from the Hippocratic corpus:

> As to those who would demolish the art [of medicine] by [reference to] fatal cases of sickness, I wonder what adequate reason induces them to hold innocent the ill-luck of the victims, and to put all the blame upon the intelligence of those who practiced the art of medicine. [Their argument] amounts to this: while physicians may give wrong instructions, patients can never disobey orders. And yet it is much more likely that the sick cannot follow out the orders than that the physicians give wrong instructions. The physician sets about his task with healthy mind and healthy body, having considered the case and past cases of like characteristics to the present, so as to say how they were treated and cured. The patient knows neither what he is suffering from, nor the cause thereof: neither what will be the outcome of his present state, nor the usual results of like conditions. In this state he receives orders, suffering in the present and fearful of the future; full of the disease, and empty of food; wishful of treatment rather to enjoy immediate alleviation of his sickness than to recover his health; not in love with death, but powerless to endure. Which is the more likely: that men in this condition obey, instead of varying, the physician's orders, or that the physician, in the condition that my account has explained above, gives improper orders? Surely it is much more likely that the physician gives proper orders, which the patient not unnaturally is unable to follow; and not following them he meets with death, the cause of which illogical reasoners attribute to the innocent, allowing the guilty to go free.[1]

The substance of this ancient claim is present, though less transparently and on a somewhat firmer foundation of professional success, in Henderson's emphasis on the sentiments[2] and in Parsons' emphasis on the "helplessness and need of help, technical incompetence, and emotional involvement" of the patient so that "a high level of rationality of judgment [is] peculiarly difficult for him."[3]

There is much that is suspect about this view. The term "irrational" is more often used in a pejorative than an analytical

---

[1] Hippocrates, *op. cit.*, vol. 2, pp. 201–203.

[2] Henderson, L. J., "Physician and Patient as a Social System," *New England Journal of Medicine*, vol. 212, May 2, 1935, pp. 819–823.

[3] Parsons, Talcott, *op. cit.*, pp. 440, 446.

sense. Like our Hippocratic writer, professionals themselves define their truth, fragile though it may be, and call resistance to it
"irrational." We may not doubt that most patients are sometimes prey to anxiety and become truly irrational but it is not
irrational to seek an independent opinion or a therapeutic procedure that worked in the past. The idea of the irrational patient
is at best a very partial truth that explains a rather small part of
patient resistance. Since it is commonly used indiscriminately, its
net function is to deprecate the patient's capacity to be right
when he contradicts the doctor. Thus, it may be seen as an
element of professional ideology that tries to justify the control
that the professional seeks over his client.

### The Role of the Physician in Reducing Conflict

The idea that the patient is irrational suggests that he cannot
really adjust himself to the doctor's expectations. Henderson
emphasized the importance of the "sentiments" in motivating the
patient, and consequently the importance for the physician to
take those sentiments into consideration in dealing with the patient.[1] The same idea is advanced in the context of patient "ignorance," particularly by those concerned with the fate of fairly
exotic patients who cannot be expected to become "educated"
quickly.[2] These writers suggest that the physician should be able
to get patients to consult him and reduce conflict during consultation by adjusting himself to the patient's expectations. If, for
example, his prospective patients ignorantly or irrationally interpret the professional attitude of detachment and impersonality to
be hostile, the doctor should be prepared to behave in a less
"professional" and more sociable way.[3] On the whole, the recent
movement to bring social science into the curriculum of American
medical schools assumes that by teaching the prospective physician more about "the patient as a person," he will be better

[1] Henderson, L. J., *op. cit.*, p. 821.

[2] Works by Saunders and Paul have already been cited. Also relevant are *Cultural Patterns and Technical Change*, edited by Margaret Mead, New American Library, New York, 1955; and Clark, Margaret, *Health in the Mexican-American Culture*, University of California Press, Berkeley, Calif., 1959.

[3] Clark, Margaret, *op. cit.*, p. 215.

equipped to understand and tolerate those expectations of the patient that contradict his own and by adjusting himself to them, reduce conflict.

But how far can we expect the physician to adjust himself to the patient's lay (and sometimes bizarre) expectations without ceasing to practice modern medicine? There is, of course, a great practical difference between automatic and rigid compliance to a set of scholastic propositions and a more flexible kind of behavior, and certainly professionals would agree that the latter is likely to be the better of the two. But flexibility must remain within limits or it becomes "irresponsible." The physician can listen closely to the patient and adjust to him only so far. If his adjustment is too great, the physician denies the heritage of special knowledge that marks him off as a professional—in effect he ceases to be a professional. Thus, we may say that some conflict in the physician-patient relationship may, indeed, be forestalled by educating physicians to be somewhat more understanding and flexible with patients, but that there is a line beyond which the physician cannot go and remain a physician. Some patients' expectations cannot be met.

### The Role of Constraint in Controlling Conflict

The patient, properly educated or not, will find occasion to resist the doctor. The doctor cannot accommodate himself to the patient beyond a certain point without ceasing to be a professional expert, but his expert status does not by itself stimulate patient cooperation in the areas where conflict is most likely to occur. Each of the elements we have discussed has some bearing on the reduction of conflict but none is wholly adequate, and a residue seems to remain. This residue of conflict, I believe, cannot be resolved. It can only be managed by forms of control that are logically quite independent of the sick role and the role of professional expert.

As Gouldner has observed,[1] we may distinguish between the

---

[1] See Gouldner, Alvin W., "Cosmopolitans and Locals: Toward an Analysis of Latent Social Roles—I," *Administrative Science Quarterly*, vol. 2, December, 1957, pp. 281–286.

characteristics of a person that are generally agreed to be relevant and legitimate to his performance of a role (his *manifest identity*) and those that may or may not be recognized to exist, and which are generally considered irrelevant or illegitimate (his *latent identity*). The physician's manifest identity is that of an expert. The physician's latent identity includes his class position in the community outside the consulting-room. Theoretically, his skill as a doctor has nothing to do with his class position, but his class position provides or withholds the leverage the doctor needs to control his patients so that he may practice his skill without compromise.

Latent identity seems crucial for sustaining the force of manifest identity. While many occupations possess expert knowledge, few have been able to gain extensive control over the terms of their work. The established professions—law, theology, medicine —have gained control over their work not by demonstrating any unusually efficacious knowledge, when all is said and done, but by gaining political power to control the socio-legal framework of practice, and by attaining social prestige to control the client in consultation. Both the power of the profession and the prestige of the practitioner seem to be critical conditions for controlling doctor-patient conflict *without* compromising expert knowledge. However, even when professional power and technical expertness are high, the relative prestige of the practitioner varies. It is not a constant. It has varied through history; within any particular society it varies from one practitioner to another; within any particular practice it can vary from one patient to another.

When the physician has had a *lower* standing than his patient, is "more on a footing with the servants,"[1] he seems to have been obliged to be either complaisant or nimble, or both, to preserve the relationship. This necessity is clearest in instances where social standing was accompanied by absolute power and the severest result could ensue from failure. For example:

Astragasilde, Queen of France, on her death bed had begged her husband, Gontrano, to throw her doctor out of the window immedi-

[1] Eliot, George, *Middlemarch: A Study of Provincial Life.* A. L. Burt Co., New York, n.d., p. 91.

ately after her death, which was done with the greatest punctuality.
. . . In the fifteenth century, John XXII burned an unsuccessful
physician at Florence and, on this Pope's death, his friends flayed the
surgeon who had failed to keep him alive.[1]

Under such circumstances the difficulties of practice according
to strictly professional standards must be very great indeed—
beyond fear of severe punishment for failure, considerable frustration could be caused by the way a patient of relatively high
standing could effectively refuse to cooperate, as the difficulties
of Dr. Henry Atkins, physician to Charles, Duke of Albany,
indicated.[2]

Even today it is reasonable to think that physicians to the
eminent and powerful have a trying practice, and that their behavior in the presence of superordinate patients will differ considerably from their behavior in the presence of "charity" patients in a hospital outpatient clinic. Indeed, Hollingshead and
Redlich observed that upper class

> . . . patients and their families make more demands of psychiatrists
> than other patients. . . . These patients and their families usually
> view the physician as middle class. In such relationships the psychi-
> atrist is not in a position to exert social power; he is lucky if he is able
> to rely on professional techniques successfully. All too often he has to
> carry out complicated maneuvers vis-a-vis a critical, demanding,
> sometimes informed, and sometimes very uninformed "VIP." Some
> VIP's push the physician into the role of lackey or comforter, and
> some psychiatrists fall into such a role.[3]

Obviously, where the relative latent status of the physician is
below that of the patient, he is not in a very good position to
obtain cooperation. Where the patient resists him, he is likely
to give in.

[1] Riesman, David, *The Story of Medicine in the Middle Ages*. Paul B. Hoeber, Inc.,
New York, 1935, p. 365. And we may cite the physician John, who was notable in
that he was *not* executed when his patient, Henry I of France, died. He was merely
nicknamed "The Deaf" afterward, for he claimed that he did not hear the King ask
for a contraindicated drink of water. MacKinney, Loren C., *Early Medieval Medicine
with Special Reference to France and Chartres*. The Johns Hopkins Press, Baltimore, 1937,
pp. 143–144.

[2] Keevil, J. J. "The Illness of Charles, Duke of Albany, (Charles I), from 1600
to 1612: An Historical Case of Rickets," *Journal of the History of Medicine and Allied
Sciences*, vol. 9, October, 1954, pp. 410–414.

[3] Hollingshead, August B., and Frederick C. Redlich, *Social Class and Mental Illness*. John Wiley and Sons, New York, 1958, p. 353. See also pp. 326–327, 338.

On the other side, we have a situation in which the physician has considerably higher standing than the patient—for example, James IV, King of Scotland, who tried his hand at blood-letting and tooth-pulling.[1] Here, while the physician's behavior might be qualified by his sense of paternalistic or professional responsibility, we should expect that his standing is sufficiently intimidating to the patient that, during the time that the patient is in his hands, he will be in a position to impose the full weight of his professional knowledge. However, as Simmons has observed, "The deference doctors receive as upper-status persons can easily be mistaken for voluntary respect and confidence. This error could prevent perception of substantial resentments and resistances of patients."[2] The patient may avoid going to see the doctor in the first place—King James, as a matter of fact, paid his subjects a fee to get them to use his services. The patient may play dumb, listen politely while in the consulting-room and, once outside, ignore the physician's advice. Evasive techniques being common in instances where the physician is in a position to intimidate his patients, we find another dilemma: the physician who is subordinate to his patient may have to compromise his knowledge; if he is superordinate, the patient may avoid him altogether and so destroy his practice.

### The Problem of a Model for Doctor-Patient Relationships

The tangle of dilemmas uncovered in our analysis of the elements of the doctor-patient relationship may make it appear that the practice of medicine is an impossible undertaking. Not at all—only the ideally professional practice of medicine is an impossible undertaking. Reality swings between the horns of dilemmas and medical practice is no exception. The doctor-patient relationship and the medical practice in which it exists are compromises between conflicting needs, demands, and forces.

[1] Guthrie, Douglas, "King James the Fourth of Scotland: His Influence on Medicine and Science," *Bulletin of the History of Medicine*, vol. 21, March-April, 1947, pp. 180–183.

[2] Simmons, Ozzie G., *Social Status and Public Health*. Pamphlet no. 13, Social Science Research, New York, 1958, p. 22. Simmons hopefully suggests that equal latent status will allow the intrinsic client and consultant roles to operate unhindered, and so encourage optimal cooperation. The evidence I have presented from The Bronx throws doubt on this optimism.

Confronted by this tension-ridden, unstable phenomenon, we have a very real problem of ordering our understanding. Concepts are stable and fixed—by their very stability we are able to order an array of individual cases. However, concepts have little value if they do not pick out salient features of reality, and in the case of the doctor-patient relationship the reality is sufficiently fluid to make it difficult to know exactly what concepts would be most useful.

A rather popular way of conceptualizing the doctor-patient relationship lies in constructing a formal model based on how physician and patient *should* behave. This sort of model underlies much of the hortatory writing of professionals about themselves and their patients. In a more neutral, elegant, and empirically useful way it also forms the basis for Talcott Parson's analysis.[1] From Parsons' analysis of role-expectations we learn that the physician is supposed to avoid emotional involvement in the patient or his plight, to restrict his activities to those in which he is professionally competent, to treat every patient the same way irrespective of his sex, race, socioeconomic status, and so on. The patient is supposed to seek technically competent help, to submit to professional authority, to suspend his emotional involvement in his own plight, and so on.

The virtue of this kind of analysis is that it provides us with a definition of (philosophically) the "essence" of the relationship. We may use it as a fixed standard by which we may measure the variable deviations of reality. However, it cannot really explain reality. It can only say what reality should be and note exceptions: it can note that the patient should submit to professional authority but, in fact, does not.

The deficiency of the approach does not entirely lie in its emphasis on ideal expectations rather than actual behavior. Parsons seems to derive his definition of the sick role from one quite limited perspective—the physician's. Much more of reality could be traced intelligibly if definition of the doctor-patient relationship could pay attention to all the perspectives involved

[1] Parsons, Talcott, *op. cit.*, pp. 428–479.

in what Merton calls the "role-set."[1] The sick role, for example, might be defined not in general, or from one point of view, but from the points of view of the patient himself, of his lay associates, of the physician, and, if in a hospital, of the nurses and any other persons significant to the process of treatment. By so doing we could anticipate and explain the conflict that appears in the doctor-patient relationship by pointing to the varying expectations of all the members of the role-set.

Superior as this modified approach may be, however, it is still not quite enough. It does not allow us to determine the weight we must assign to each perspective, and so does not allow us to assess the importance of each perspective in exacerbating or reducing conflict. An expectation, like an attitude or an opinion, has no influence in itself. Simply the fact that two patients expect with about the same intensity that their doctor take an interest in them does not mean that their doctor will take equal interest in each. The response to an expectation is at least a partial function of the influence lying behind the person with that expectation.[2] Influence does not inhere in the expectation, but in the position of the person holding it. In addition, the very possibility of conforming to an expectation is a partial function of the limits imposed by the situation in which that expectation is expressed.

In order to understand and predict the chances that an expectation will be met, then, it is not enough to specify the expectations of everyone included in the doctor's or patient's role-set. Attention must be paid to the social structure in which those perspectives are located, and there must be systematic specification of the variable situations and positions of influence in which doctors and patients find themselves. Furthermore, as this chapter has argued, it is realistic to see the relationship as a form of conflict,[3] the compromise of practice shifting now one way, now another, as the influence of the participants' positions shifts.

[1] Merton, Robert K., op. cit.

[2] Ibid., p. 113.

[3] For expression of a point of view with which I feel kinship, see Dahrendorf, Ralf, "Out of Utopia: Toward a Reorientation of Sociological Analysis," American Journal of Sociology, vol. 64, September, 1958, pp. 115-127.

# 10. The Structure of Doctor-Patient Relationships[1]

A MODEL OF THE STRUCTURE of doctor-patient relationships must encompass two distinct social systems—a professional system containing the doctor and a lay system containing the patient. Furthermore, these systems must be part of a larger whole from which doctor and patient derive latent identities. The concept of the community will be used to represent that whole. In order that doctor and patient be brought together in consultation, the systems that nurture them must be seen to overlap or intersect, and some mechanism must be postulated by which individuals are drawn through the systems. The referral will be used as that mechanism. Finally, there must be some means of focusing and ordering variation in the balance of constraints in the conflict between doctor and patient. The position of practice in both the lay and professional referral processes will be used to define variation and predict its outcome.

## The Community

The community forms the outermost practical framework for the doctor-patient relationship. In discussions of the nature of the community a conventional contrast is made between the small, isolated, nonindustrial communities characteristic of "primitive" society and the great urban settlements characteristic of modern industrial society. In the former, which are characteristically isolated from other communities and homogeneous in composi-

[1] Portions of this chapter have already appeared in Freidson, Eliot, "Client Control and Medical Practice," *American Journal of Sociology*, vol. 65, January, 1960, pp. 374–382. Reprinted by permission of the University of Chicago Press.

tion, human relations are predominantly long-term, personal, and centered around the family and the locality. In the latter, which are characteristically in continuous contact with other communities and rather heterogeneous, relationships are predominantly brief, impersonal and individualistic, centering around the market place.[1] In the city, personal relations are seen to be fleeting and shallow, to involve on many occasions only small segments of the individual's total personality.[2] The urbanite, like the member of the mass,[3] acts more as an individual than as a closely controlled member of persistent social groups.

True as the contrast between folk and urban community is, however, it is of only limited value. It stresses conditions that account for much of the rapid change to be observed in modern society, but fails to explain the fact that considerably less change takes place than one might expect from efforts made to induce it, and that what changes do occur are rather circumscribed in content and direction.[4] Experience is not so atomized as one might expect; there is more organization than may at first appear.

Empirically, it has been found that while there is mobility and isolation in the modern urban community, a large segment of the population stays put for a respectable period of time and spends its leisure within a fairly limited, persistent, and intimate circle of kin, friends, and neighbors.[5] Many urban residents have little

[1] For a clear statement of the contrast see Redfield, Robert, *Folk Culture of Yucatan*, University of Chicago Press, Chicago, 1941.

[2] See Wirth, Louis, "Urbanism as a Way of Life" in *Reader in Urban Sociology*, edited by Paul K. Hatt and Albert J. Reiss, The Free Press, Glencoe, Ill., 1951, pp. 32–49; and Simmel, Georg, "The Metropolis and Mental Life," *ibid.*, pp. 563–574.

[3] For the classic definition of the "mass," see Blumer, Herbert, "Collective Behavior" in *New Outline of the Principles of Sociology*, edited by A. M. Lee, Barnes and Noble, Inc., New York, 1946, pp. 167–222. See also Freidson, Eliot, "Communications Research and the Concept of the Mass," *American Sociological Review*, vol. 18, June, 1953, pp. 316–317.

[4] See, for example, the assessments of the limited effects of propaganda: Lazarsfeld, Paul F., and Robert K. Merton, "Mass Communication, Popular Taste and Organized Social Action" in *Mass Communications*, edited by Wilbur Schramm, University of Illinois Press, Urbana, 1949, pp. 457–480; and Berelson, Bernard, "Communications and Public Opinion," *ibid.*, pp. 496–512.

[5] Samples of American studies are the following: Smith, Joel, William H. Form, and Gregory P. Stone, "Local Intimacy in a Middle-sized City," *American Journal of Sociology*, vol. 60, November, 1954, pp. 276–284; Foley, Donald L., "The Use of Local Facilities in a Metropolis," *American Journal of Sociology*, vol. 56, November, 1950, pp. 238–246; Bell, Wendell, and Marion D. Boat, "Urban Neighborhoods and Informal Social Relations," *American Journal of Sociology*, vol. 62, January, 1957, pp. 391–398; Litwak, Eugene, "Geographic Mobility and Family Cohesion," *American Sociological Review*, vol. 25, June, 1960, pp. 385–394.

to do with impersonal and segmental voluntary associations, and consider them to be outside of, even foreign and antagonistic to, their interests and affairs.[1] Interpersonal influence remains important in human affairs, and close networks of social relationships organize and guide the behavior of the individual in the urban world.[2] The metropolis may, indeed, be a heterogeneous "mosaic of social worlds in which the transition from one to the other is abrupt,"[3] but individuals within it spend their most formative hours in their own small, local, and personal world within that mosaic. The force of change lies in ideological and material elements that are outside the neighborhood, pressing in on it. The force of persistence lies in the network that mediates and controls the influence of the outside. The social psychological concept of personal influence[4] and the structural concept of the social network refer to the resources of the neighborhood in its struggle with the outside.

The traditional contrast between urban and folk communities provides no clear, organized basis for dealing with the force of persistence. Since it has proved critical to our understanding of patients in The Bronx, some other conception of community is needed to serve as our framework for analyzing the structure of doctor-patient relationships. The image that seems most appropriate is based upon Redfield's discussion of peasant society. In peasant society are "rural people in old civilizations . . . who control and cultivate their land for subsistence and as a part of a traditional way of life and who look to and are influenced by gentry or townspeople whose way of life is like theirs but in a more civilized form."[5] The reference to agriculture is for our purposes irrelevant, but what is useful is the suggestion of a

[1] This is best communicated by qualitative studies such as Kerr, Madeline, *The People of Ship Street*, Routledge and Kegan Paul, London, 1958; and Hoggart, Richard, *The Uses of Literacy*, Essential Books, Inc., Fairlawn, N. J., 1957.

[2] Elizabeth Bott's "Urban Families: Conjugal Roles and Social Networks" (*Human Relations*, vol. 8, 1955, pp. 345–384) contains a very important attempt to define the nature and significance of such networks and their place in urban life.

[3] Wirth, Louis, *op. cit.*, p. 42.

[4] See Katz, Elihu, and Paul F. Lazarsfeld, *Personal Influence*, The Free Press, Glencoe, Ill., 1955.

[5] Redfield, Robert, *Peasant Society and Culture*. University of Chicago Press, Chicago, 1956, p. 31.

cultural and structural division between residents in the community—"local people," and the local representatives of national institutions. We may see in the city as in the village "continual communication to the local community of thought originating outside of it. The intellectual and often the religious life of the [local community] is perpetually incomplete."[1] Thus, we may distinguish between "a great tradition of the reflective few, and . . . a little tradition of the largely unreflective many. The great tradition is cultivated in schools or temples; the little tradition works itself out and keeps itself going in the lives of the unlettered in their [local] communities."[2]

Medicine may be seen as one of the "great traditions." In modern and often in ancient civilizations it has consisted in a body of technique and knowledge sustained by educational institutions that participate in an extralocal life. Practitioners are trained within those institutions and so gain their professional knowledge and identity.[3] Thus, in the lay communities in which they practice, physicians are in the same structural position as the gentry, the official and the priest in peasant society—representatives of the outside, with knowledge that does not originate in the community and may not be current within it. They are part of both local and "outside" worlds, though individuals may variously orient themselves locally or to the outside.[4]

Contrast between two parts of the community is even more significant for modern than for ancient communities, since there is emerging an increasingly sharp distinction between those who are supposed to know (and are therefore responsible for speaking with authority and making decisions) and those who do not know (and who are therefore responsible for submitting to others'

[1] *Ibid.*, p. 68.

[2] *Ibid.*, p. 70.

[3] For a discussion of professional identity see Goode, William J., "Community Within a Community: The Professions," *American Sociological Review*, vol. 22, April, 1957, pp. 194–200.

[4] The distinction between "locals" and "cosmopolitans" (cf. Gouldner, Alvin W., "Cosmopolitans and Locals: Toward an Analysis of Latent Social Roles—I," *Administrative Science Quarterly*, vol. 2, December, 1957, pp. 281–286) refers to the way in which individuals orient themselves irrespective of their positions. Thus, a "native" of a town might conceivably be a "cosmopolitan." The distinction I make is structural rather than social psychological.

decisions).[1]    Professional knowledge is perhaps the major "great tradition" of our day. While in the past, as Redfield noted,[2] elements of the little tradition were slowly adopted and woven into the great tradition—the two being at least partially inter-dependent—the professional knowledge of our present time is increasingly independent of lay understanding. The great tradition of our time no longer borrows from the little; the little is expected to accommodate itself to the great.

## Practice as the Clash of Two Worlds

We can imagine the community to be an incomplete circle, its walls breeched by one or more structures that originate outside it. Within the walls is a series of small, sometimes inter-locking networks of local people, in occasional contact with the representatives of the invading professional or official structure. The influence of the specialist or consultant rests theoretically on his connection with the world outside; the influence of local social networks rests on sympathy and shared experience. The "tradition" of the specialist is officially channeled and sustained by public means of communication, informally by colleague net-works; the "tradition" of the layman is created, channeled, and sustained by informal and intimate modes of communication.[3] The practicing physician is the hinge between the two systems.

Characteristically, the professional practitioner claims that his skills are so esoteric that the client is in no position to evaluate them. Consonant with that claim is his privilege to be somewhat

[1] For views of the "expert" in the lay community, see Seeley, John R., and others, *Crestwood Heights*, Basic Books, Inc., New York, 1956, Chapter 11, Layman and Expert, pp. 343–377, and particularly Vidich, Arthur J., and Joseph Bensman, *Small Town in Mass Society*, Anchor Books, New York, 1960, pp. 199–201, 236–245.

[2] Redfield, Robert, *op. cit.*, p. 71.

[3] This means of communication has received far too little study. In our society, where mass media of communication are supposed to be so pervasive, there is still a whole "underworld" of at least quasi-mass communications that go on almost en-tirely by word of mouth. An example of this, the more interesting because almost never transmitted by the mass media, is the "dirty" joke or others that are in "poor taste." In countries where the state monopolizes the mass media, political jokes sometimes are officially banned and circulate quite widely independently of the mass media.

Children's rhymes and jokes also have a startling circulation and persistence in this world of presumed change, again independently of the mass media. On these see Opie, Iona and Peter, *The Lore and Language of Schoolchildren*, Oxford University Press, New York, 1960.

removed from the market place and to submit to the judgment of no one but his colleagues. The claim is one symptom of his sense of professional identity. But he must practice in a local community among laymen. While he may share special knowledge, loyalty, and identity with his colleagues rather than with laymen, he is dependent upon laymen for his livelihood.

Except in special institutions like factories and schools or in some public health situations, the physician does not have the power to force laymen to use his services. His practice is dependent upon their free choice to use medical rather than nonmedical services, and in some circumstances to use his services rather than those of other physicians. However, his prospective clients are in no position to evaluate his services in the same way as would his colleagues. Insofar as they exercise choice, it must be made on the basis of nonprofessional criteria; they will interact with him on the basis of the nonprofessional norms of their lay traditions. While the lay tradition may, in one place or another, absorb varying amounts of the professional, it is unlikely to become identical with the professional tradition[1] and is always potentially in conflict with it. The professional tradition can be kept quite undefiled in such institutions as medical schools, but it cannot help coming into contact with lay tradition in medical practice. Indeed, in a sense its very existence is threatened by lay tradition. Practice is the focus for the clash between the two worlds.

## The Referral Mechanism

Given the two systems, how are they brought into contact? By what mechanism is consultation initiated? Obviously, the prospective patient must believe that he is ill, or otherwise needs help. Furthermore, he must in some way diagnose his difficulty so as to know what to do about it. At the very least a diagnosis implies some kind of treatment of the problem—staying in bed, taking vitamins, going for a vacation, getting a divorce, or whatever. Often enough the implied treatment requires the services of a person other than the sufferer—a druggist, a lawyer, a clergyman, a physician. When this occurs, implicit in diagnosis is

[1] See Saunders, Lyle W., and G. H. Hewes, "Folk Medicine and Medical Practice," *Journal of Medical Education*, vol. 28, September, 1953, pp. 43–46.

designation of the person who may properly administer or advise treatment. One side of diagnosis is thus definition of the difficulty and its treatment; another is referral to consultants or therapists. When the consultants or therapists themselves diagnose the problem, they may treat it themselves or they may refer it to another person.

We saw that in The Bronx the process of seeking help began with purely personal, tentative self-diagnoses that implied their own self-administered treatments. Upon failure of those first prescriptions, members of the household were consulted. Aid in self-diagnosis was sometimes sought from laymen outside the household—friends, neighbors, relatives, fellow-workers, a former nurse, or someone with the same trouble. Indeed, when exploration of diagnoses was drawn out and not stopped early by cessation of symptoms or immediate recourse to a physician, the prospective patient referred himself or was referred through a hierarchy of consultant positions. The hierarchy ran from the intimate and informal confines of the nuclear family through successively less intimate lay consultants until the professional was finally reached.

As a tool of analysis, the concept of the referral allows us to trace how consultation between patient and doctor is initiated. It is an act that bridges consultant positions and allows us to find a sequential structure in the process of seeking help: experience can be ordered by reference to the hierarchy of consultants to whom the patient is referred. As an act common to both lay and professional worlds in spite of the sometimes vast cultural differences between them, it allows us to define two referral structures, one leading into the other. Each consultant position, lay or professional, may itself be seen as a kind of "practice," but we will focus here on the implications of referral to professional positions in the structures in order to gain an idea of the qualifying conditions for the use of medical services.

## Types of Lay Referral Systems

How does variation in the lay referral system affect the conditions for consulting a physician? If we were to look literally we would find as many lay referral systems as there are social networks, but it is possible to classify all by two critical variables—the degree of congruence between the cultures of the prospective clientele and the profession, and the relative number and cohesiveness of lay consultants who are interposed between the first perception of symptoms and the decision to see a professional.[1] Consideration of culture has relevance to the diagnoses and prescriptions that are meaningful to the client, and to the kinds of consultants believed authoritative. Consideration of the extensiveness of the lay referral structure has relevance to the channeling and reinforcement of lay culture and to the flowing-in of "outside" communications. These variables may be combined so as to yield four types of lay referral system.

First there is a system in which the prospective clients participate primarily in an indigenous lay culture and in which there is a highly extended, cohesive lay referral structure. In the indigenous extended system the clientele may be expected to show a high degree of resistance to using medical services. If, for example, prospective patients are prone to believe that hereditary or divine gift is prerequisite to diagnostic competence, professional authority is unlikely to be recognized at all. And if, for example, they believe that illness is caused by supernatural forces[2] the referral will not often lead to a physician either. Furthermore, the force of cultural difference is intensified by the extended referral structure. Anyone inclined to try a professional practitioner must first run a gauntlet of anti-professional advice. Obviously, the folk practitioner will be used by most. The professional practitioner is likely to be called only for minor illness or, in illness considered critical, called by the socially isolated deviate[3] and the desperate man clutching at straws.

---

[1] Following Bott, we might also contrast a "highly connected network" in which "many of the individuals know and meet one another independently of [their common acquaintance] X," and a "dispersed network," in which "few of the individuals in X's network know and meet one another independently of X." Bott, Elizabeth, *op. cit.*, p. 348.

[2] For a superb analysis of such beliefs, as well as material on the referral structure of a non-European society, see Evans-Pritchard, E. E., *Witchcraft, Oracles and Magic Among the Azande*, Clarendon Press, Oxford, 1937.

[3] The hypothesis of the deviate as innovator is conventional but by no means obviously true, and may have to be qualified considerably when the refined evidence we need is gathered. For careful consideration of the hypothesis, see Menzel, Herbert, "Innovation, Integration, and Marginality: A Survey of Physicians," *American Sociological Review*, vol. 25, October, 1960, pp. 704–713.

The second type of lay referral system has the same indigenous culture as the first, but a truncated referral structure—the individual may act entirely on his own, or at least consult no layman outside the nuclear family. The culture of the system discourages the use of a physician, but lacking an extended network of interpersonal influence to reinforce the culture, the individual is more vulnerable to outside influence and, all else being equal, may be expected to try a physician sooner and under less desperate circumstances than a person in the indigenous extended system.

The third type is the opposite of the indigenous extended lay referral system. It is found when lay and professional culture are very much alike, and when the lay referral structure is truncated. The prospective client is pretty much on his own, guided more or less by his own understandings and experience, with few lay consultants to support or discourage his search for help. Since his knowledge and understandings are much like the physician's he may take a great deal of time trying to treat himself for disorders he feels competent to deal with, but nonetheless will go directly from self-treatment to a physician. He may resist the physician, but his resistance will be manipulative rather than evasive. He is unlikely to use a nonmedical healer until he is desperate.

He is even less likely to use the services of a nonmedical healer in the fourth type of lay referral system. Since it has an extended referral structure and a culture similar to the professional's, his acceptance of professional culture is considerably more likely to be reinforced than is the case of a professionally oriented person who participates in a truncated structure.

## Lay Controls on Practice

As Goode has noted, "Client choices are a form of social control. They determine the survival of a profession or a specialty, as well as the career success of particular professionals."[1] The concept of the lay referral system provides a basis for organizing knowledge about the extent and the potency of cultural difference between doctor and patient. Since that difference con-

[1] Goode, William J., *op. cit.*, p. 198.

ditions client choices, it allows us to understand how the layman can control professional practice by threatening its survival. It not only tells us why a practitioner may never get any clients but also why he may get but then lose them.

The lay referral system may not only channel the patient's choice away from a particular physician, but even if it first leads to him it may later on move the patient to change his mind and go elsewhere. We may remember that the first visit to a practitioner is often tentative, a tryout. Whether the physician's prescription is followed or not, and whether the patient comes back, often seem to rest at least partly on his retrospective assessment of the consultation. The client may compare notes with others, and thus pass through the lay referral structure not only on his way to the physician but also on his way back. One consequence of discussion with his fellows of the doctor's behavior, diagnosis, and prescription may be that he resolves never to go back. It is reasonable to assume that all but the most thick-skinned entrepreneurial practitioners soon become aware of lay evaluations, whether through their patients' repeated requests for vitamins or wonder drugs or, in times past, through disappearance or protest following the employment of unpopular prescriptions like calomel or bleeding. Their motive may be to heal the patient or it may be merely to survive professionally, but in either case physicians will feel pressure to accept or manipulate lay expectations, whether by administering placebos[1] or by giving up unpopular procedures.[2]

In a community, then, channels of influence and authority that exist independently of the profession may guide the patient toward or away from the physician. By so doing they may control the physician's success and influence his very professional manner and technique of practice. Practice in a culturally indigenous and extended lay system must adjust itself to the system from the very

[1] The placebo might be used as an index of control by the client of the terms of practice. On rationalizing sleight-of-hand as a placebo, see Evans-Pritchard, E. E., *op. cit.*, pp. 235–236.

[2] "This helplessness of regular physicians, coupled with popular distaste for bleeding and vile medicines, goes far to explain the success enjoyed by large groups of irregular practitioners. . . . A not uncommon shingle advertisement in those early years was: Dr. John Doe. No Calomel." Bonner, Thomas Neville, *Medicine in Chicago, 1850–1950*. American History Research Center, Madison, Wis., 1957, p. 12.

beginning in order to survive; under other circumstances it need make, up to a certain point at least, fewer adjustments.

## Professional Controls on Laymen

The discussion thus far should be taken to show that the physician has only relative freedom from control by patients, not absolute freedom. This being so, it seems fruitful to classify medical practices by their degree of professional freedom. A useful principle of classification may be derived from examination of the source of referrals.

Enough has been written about the privileged position that the organized power of the state grants the professional practitioner. Support by power located outside the community is often crucial to practice in "underdeveloped" countries where the prospective patients do not have a high opinion of modern physicians. Even in modern societies, relative freedom from patient control is strengthened by political support that sets severe limitation on competition by prosecuting irregular "folk" or "quack" practice, by allowing restriction of the number of professional practitioners, and by restricting the drugs that may be bought without prescription. The reduction of competition greatly contributes to the stability and autonomy of the professional role and cannot be overestimated.[1]

Beyond these measures, however, we may note another source of strength in the "professional referral system." The professional referral system is a structure or network of relationships with colleagues that often extends beyond the local community, but that tends to converge on such professionally controlled organizations as hospitals, medical societies, and medical schools. Professional prestige and power radiate out of those organizations and diminish with distance from them. The authoritative source of

[1] To cite a dramatic instance of the kind of behavior that stemmed from competition: two tenth century physicians who were competing for the favor of a king ended by poisoning each other at the king's dinner table. The one who knew the antidotes obtained the king's patronage. MacKinney, L. C., "Tenth Century Medicine as Seen in the *Historia* of Richer of Rheims," *Bulletin of the History of Medicine*, vol. 2, August, 1934, pp. 367–368.
The veracity of Richer's account is questioned in Kristeller, P. O., "The School of Salerno," *Bulletin of the History of Medicine*, vol. 17, February, 1945, pp. 143–144, but as the historian Louis Gottschalk once said, "Se non è vero è ben trovato."

professional culture—that is, medical knowledge—lies in those organizations, partly created by them and partly flowing into them from the outside.

The further within this professional referral system a practice is located, the more free the practitioner is of control by clients; the patient finds that there are fewer choices he can make and that he has less control over what is done to him. Indeed, it is not unknown for the patient to be a petitioner asking to be chosen: the organizations and practitioners who stand well within the professional referral system may or may not "take the case," according to their judgment.

The client chooses his professional services when they are in the lay referral system, but the physician chooses the patient to whom to give his services when he is in the professional referral system. This fundamental symmetry becomes somewhat clearer when we reexamine the process of seeking help. When he first feels ill, the patient thinks he is competent to judge whether he is actually ill and what general class of illness it is. On this basis he treats himself. Failure of his initial self-prescriptions leads him to other lay consultants, and the failure of their prescriptions leads him to the physician. Upon this preliminary career of failures the practical authority of the physician rests. However, the patient's movement through the lay referral system to the first professional consultant is predicated upon the *client's* conception of what he needs. The practitioner standing at the apex of the lay referral system—who may be either a specialist or a general practitioner in the United States[1]—is chosen on the basis of that lay conception.

When the practitioner chosen by the patient cannot himself handle the problem, it may become *his* function, not that of the patient or his lay consultants, to refer to another practitioner. Of course, the patient may take it upon himself to seek another physician, but eventually he gets beyond his depth and referral does fall into professional hands. At this point choice, and therefore positive control, is out of the hands of the client and comes

[1] The actual specialty of the practitioner who stands within the lay referral system varies. Certainly the general practitioner is almost always within it. Often pediatricians, gynecologists, internists, and ophthalmologists are to be found within it. Pathologists, anesthesiologists, and radiologists are unlikely ever to be within it.

to rest in the hands of the practitioner. The use of professional services is no longer predicated on the client's lay understandings. Indeed, in the course of referral the client may be given services for which he did not ask, whose rationale is beyond him. Obviously, at this point he has become relatively helpless, divorced from his lay supports.

To the physician himself, position in the referral structure is critical. If he is the first practitioner seen during the course of lay referrals, and if he refers no cases to other physicians, he is subjected only to the evaluation of his patients and their lay consultants. If he refers a case to another practitioner, however, his professional behavior becomes potentially subject to the evaluation of the consultant. When the referred patient leaves the consultant he may pass back to the referring practitioner, so that the consultant himself is subjected to evaluation by the latter. The referring physician may exert control by the threat of ceasing to refer patients to the consultant.

### Types of Medical Practice

We see that both the physician who refers patients to colleagues and the physician who subsists on patients referred by colleagues are subject to evaluation and control by colleagues in addition to patients; in contrast, the practitioner who attracts patients himself and need not refer them to others is subject solely to evaluation and control at the hands of his patients. These observations suggest two analytical extremes of practice, differing in their relation to the lay and to the professional referral systems. The first is a practice that can operate independently of colleagues, its existence predicated on attracting its own lay clientele. In order to attract clients, this "independent practice"[1] must offer services that conform to the prejudices of the community and of a sort for which those in a lay referral system

[1] The use of the term "independent" is clearly ironic here and may be confusing, for the physician is by definition dependent upon the whims of his clients. Without extreme restriction of competition the "free professional" is about as "free" and "independent" as a small shopkeeper. We may recall the plight of the nineteenth century English sixpenny doctor "attending patients who rapped on the counter and called, 'Shop!'" Turner, Ernest S., *Call The Doctor*, St. Martin's Press, New York, 1959, p. 213. The reader may prefer the term "client-centered." In like manner, the term "colleague-centered" may be substituted for "dependent."

themselves recognize the need. It is, of course, conditioned by the existence of competitors and by the type of lay referral system in which it finds itself, but on the whole one should expect it to be incapable of succeeding unless conducted in accord with lay expectations. To survive without colleagues it must be located within a lay referral system and, as such, is least able to resist control by clients and most able to resist control by colleagues.

The second type of practice does not in and by itself attract its own clientele but, instead, serves the needs of other practices, individual or organizational. A professional colleague or an organization decides that a client needs the services of the practitioner and transmits the client to him. Expressive of this is the fact that in many cases only the colleague or organization, not the client, is told the results of the consultation. The clients with whom this "dependent practice" must deal do not choose the service involved. Obviously, in order to survive without self-selected clients, this type of practice must be located at a point in the professional referral system where clients are so helpless that they may be merely transmitted. And it must conform to the expectations of the colleagues who supply the clients. It is thus most able to resist control by clients, but least able to resist control by colleagues.

The analytical extreme of independent practice does not seem fully exemplified by any truly professional practice, for the foundation of professional practice is laid outside the lay community, in the colleague-controlled medical school and licensing board. Only the "irregular" or "quack" fits this logical extreme, since he is independent of schools and licensing bodies and therefore can, as Hughes put it, "please his customers but not his colleagues."[1] The quack, like the folk practitioner, may be seen

---

[1] Hughes, Everett C., *Men and Their Work*. The Free Press, Glencoe, Ill., 1958, p. 98. See also King, Lester S., *The Medical World of the Eighteenth Century*, University of Chicago Press, Chicago, 1958, pp. 53–54: "Quacks had this charter for their existence: they satisfied a certain number of people from whom they drew support. When they ceased to satisfy, their support stopped and they disappeared."
This definition of "quack," rather than one specifying differences in training, knowledge, and ethics, is probably the soundest to be found. As Dr. Walker observed, "As for quacks being ignorant and empirical in their methods, why, the whole medical profession is in precisely the same state as they are." Walker, Kenneth, *Patients and Doctors*. Pelican Books, Baltimore, 1957, p. 99.

as a consultant relatively high in the structure of lay referrals, with no necessary connection to an outside system.

Professionals may not reach this extreme, but they can come close to it, as we can see from Sorbière's seventeenth-century French document.[1] In the United States the closest example is found in the solo neighborhood practice, usually general in nature, that Hall called "individualistic." It has at best loose cooperative ties with colleagues and with organizations in the professional referral system.[2] All else being equal in this situation of minimal observability by colleagues and maximum dependence on the lay referral system, we should expect to find the least sensitivity to formal professional standards and the greatest sensitivity to local lay standards of practice.

Moving toward the position of dependent practice is what Hall called the "colleague practice," in close connection with a well-organized "inner fraternity" of colleagues and rigidly organized service institutions. This practice tends to revolve around specialties, which in itself makes for location outside particular neighborhoods[3] and therefore reduces the possibility of organized control by the clients.

Finally, closest to the logical extreme of dependent practice in the United States is a type which overlaps somewhat with "colleague" practice but which seems sufficiently significant to consider separately. It might be called "organizational practice." Found in hospitals, medical groups, and other professional bureaucracies, it involves maximal restriction on the client's choice of individuals or services. Clients are often referred by outside practitioners to the organization itself or to one of its departments rather than to individuals within it. If patients are seeking help on their own, their choice is restricted to selecting

[1] Pleadwell, Frank Lester, "Samuel Sorbière and his *Advice to a Young Physician*," *Bulletin of the History of Medicine*, vol. 24, May–June, 1950, pp. 255–287.

[2] See the sketch of the "inadequately trained generalist who works alone in his office virtually isolated from those in his field," in Clark, Donald M., "General Medicine" in *The Physician and His Practice*, edited by Joseph Garland, Little Brown and Co., Boston, 1954, pp. 53–54. And see Hall's papers, listed in footnote on p. 32, as well as Solomon, David, "Career Contingencies of Chicago Physicians," unpublished Ph.D. dissertation, University of Chicago, 1952.

[3] Lieberson, Stanley, "Ethnic Groups and the Practice of Medicine," *American Sociological Review*, vol. 23, October, 1958, pp. 542–549.

the organization: they are then screened by functionaries and referred to an individual practitioner. Here, practice cannot take place without the auspices of the organization, cannot be accomplished without the organization's capital equipment. The events of the referral process within the organization being systematically recorded and scrutinized, and ordered by hierarchical supervision, the practitioner is highly vulnerable to his colleagues' evaluations. We should expect him to be most sensitive to professional standards and controls and least sensitive to the expectations of his patients. The client's efforts to assert his own conceptions of his illness and its proper treatment are more likely to take the form of evasion than of self-assertion, though the better educated and the more influential he is, the better equipped is he to "make trouble."

# 11. Modern Medical Practice and the Fate of the Patient

THE TASK OF THE STUDY reported in this book was to explore the nature of the structure in which medical care takes place and to make sense of it by means of a tentative set of concepts. Its subjects were patients who subscribed to a not-at-all common type of prepaid medical-care group practice plan in The Bronx, as well as some who were the subjects of a special preventive Demonstration within the Medical Group. All of them had additional experience with entrepreneurial practitioners. Their views of those three kinds of practice were compared.

## What the Patients Wanted

The patients seemed to use two interlocking criteria to evaluate health services. First, they felt, good medical care requires technical competence. Second, they felt, good medical care requires taking an interest in the patient so that he not only obtains emotional satisfaction from the practitioner, but also the impression that competence is exercised in a more than routine way. A practitioner does not necessarily have both qualities. He can be perceived as a "good" doctor but a "cold fish," which is to say, possessing an adequate degree of technical competence but an inadequate number of the characteristics that imply his interest in the patient. And he can be perceived as "very nice," but not "up-to-date," which is to say, having an adequate degree of interest in his patient but being somewhat lacking in competence.

In general, questions of competence were raised far less than questions of interest, for under ordinary circumstances most patients assumed adequate competence. However, the patients believed that the more the technical facilities available to the physician and used by him, the better was the medicine he could practice. Most patients naturally desired what they thought to be good technical care, but they insisted nonetheless that without personal interest the practitioner could not use his full competence. The two together, then, are what the patients want.

## How Three Modes of Practice Met Patient Wants

Of the families interviewed intensively, most either had no regular relation with an entrepreneurial practitioner before they joined the Medical Group, or had experience that seriously annoyed or frightened them. Less than a third of the interviewed patients had any extended or satisfying experience with "private" medical practice, but most of them felt that personally satisfying medical care was more likely to be found in entrepreneurial practice than in the Medical Group. They believed that the entrepreneurial physician is in a better position to take interest in his patients than the Group physician. On the other hand, most of the patients did not believe it was possible for the entrepreneurial physician to give them "good" medical care; they felt that the technical facilities of the Medical Group (combined with the permissive use of diagnostic and treatment services granted by a prepayment plan) allowed Group physicians to practice "better" if not "nicer" medicine.

However, they felt that the Family Health Maintenance Demonstration had the virtues of both entrepreneurial and Medical Group practice and the deficiencies of neither. It provided them with technically good care, like the Group; and, like entrepreneurial practice, it provided them with the feeling that personal interest was being taken in them. On the whole, Family Health Maintenance Demonstration patients did *not* seem to think they obtained care that was technically superior to that provided by the Medical Group. It was the addition of personal interest to that high technical level which made Family Health Maintenance Demonstration care seem superior.

## Some Practical and Analytical Problems

Once it was quite clear that the patients liked the Demonstration, and once hints were uncovered which suggested why this kind of organization of health services was more attractive to them than the other two, the task was to determine how patient behavior accorded with patient attitudes—whether or not expressed satisfaction manifested itself in a high degree of cooperation with the professional workers of the program. The "appropriate" utilization of Demonstration services and docile following of the prescriptions of professional consultants in the Demonstration are, after all, the ultimate tests of the program's influence on its patients.

There was no objective criterion of "patient cooperation," but from the point of view of the professional workers themselves the patients' behavior left something to be desired. Attendance at health education meetings, success in the reduction of obesity, and, above all, utilization of the social workers were disappointing to the staff. In addition, it was discovered that some of the patients were going to "private" doctors for some of their care instead of using Demonstration and Group doctors. The utilization of the social worker was chosen for close attention because it allowed analysis of differential choice of varied professional services within a single organization. The utilization of "outside" doctors was chosen for examination because it permitted analysis of choice between different modes of organizing practice.

## Social Class and Patient Behavior

Social class was found to order both sets of data. Using years of education and occupational standing as measures of social class, it was found that the upper-middle class group tended to use both surgical and nonsurgical outside services to a greater extent than the lower class group. Ability to pay for outside services is obviously involved, but it was not the only or necessarily most important variable. In a survey of Medical Group subscribers it was found that high social class was associated with a greater degree of sensitivity to social stimuli in the doctor-patient relationship, and with a critical and manipulative approach to medical care. In contrast, the lower classes were less sensitive about their status as patients and were rather more passive and uncritical in their approach to medical care.

Class differences were also quite clear in patient responses to the various workers of the Family Health Maintenance Demonstration. Most patients valued their relation with the physician more than with any other worker in the Demonstration. The nurse, identified with him as a medical worker, was considered second in importance to him: she was the alternative to him for a variety of problems and more accessible, more likely to be consulted in a highly informal, personal context. The social worker was as accessible, but most often third choice.

*Within* this general pattern of choice, neither middle nor lower class was much different in perceived use of the physician, but there was a consistent tendency for the upper-middle class to choose the nurse less and the social worker more than the lower class. More of the upper-middle than the lower group considered the social worker to be an important addition to the health team. For a variety of problems the upper-middle class patients were more likely to choose consultation with the social worker than were the lower class; the lower class patients were more likely to choose the nurse.

## The Lay Referral System and the Use of Services

In almost every instance involving the use of the public health nurse for aid in problems that might be considered emotional, the patients explained their choice by reference to their belief that it was "natural" to see the nurse because they knew her and she knew them, and by reference to the belief that the problem was not "serious" enough to require the services of the social worker. The social worker's role, by its very restriction to specialized problems, seemed removed from the course of everyday affairs. As a specialist, she could not appropriately be approached during the early, essentially casual stage of seeking help without the implication that the problem had become critical. The public health nurse's role, however, by its very generality and second choice accessibility, found a place in the early stage of seeking help. Thus, it seemed that the social worker stood in an entirely different relation to the lay referral system than did the nurse. Referral to the social worker by other members of the staff was unlikely to be effective until the patient felt that the efficacy of more common remedies and less threatening definitions of the problem had been exhausted. It might have been different had referral been made to a social worker in the role of a technical aide rather than a specialist professional.

## Lay and Professional Referral Systems

In discussing the utilization of the social worker, not only were the stages of the career of seeking help mentioned, but also the way her services were organized. In this sense utilization was examined as a function of the relationship between the way a professional service is organized and the way the layman seeks help. We could contrast the organization of social worker and public health nurse roles from this point of view, and go on to contrast in the same way the organization of solo practice and Medical Group practice. (Since the Family Health Maintenance Demonstration was carried on within the Medical Group, we could in most cases treat it as a variant rather than a distinct third organization.) In so doing we were concerned with the stage at which help was being sought, with variable definitions of what it was that was needed for help, and with lay influences on the definition of what was needed at any particular stage. We were less concerned with the content of lay influence than we were with its organization and the direction of its referrals. The organization of the Medical Group and of solo practice could be compared by examining their linkage with lay referral structures.

It appeared that in comparison to solo practice the organization of the Medical Group was handicapped by its relation to the lay referral structures of its patients. The patients of the Medical Group were recruited on the basis of their places of work, while those of the solo practitioner were apparently recruited on the basis of locality and lay reputation. Analysis of the contrast suggested that when the Medical Group patient seeks advice from his lay consultants, they are not likely to be members of his

Medical Group and so he is at least as likely to be referred by them to an outside physician as he is to a Medical Group practitioner. This is particularly the case if they are as knowledgeable about "outside" resources as the upper-middle class patients' consultants.

Lay pressure seems even more significant in the light of the problem of obtaining medical opinions. While the patients who were interviewed manifested little doubt that the opinion of one solo practitioner was independent of others, some did express doubt about the independence of medical opinions within the Medical Group. As a cooperative enterprise, the ties between Group practitioners were manifest and public, so that some patients found it difficult to accept one Group practitioner's testimony on the excellence of another otherwise unknown Group practitioner. For those patients, reputations had to be established independently of the professional workers of the Group—by an outside physician or by a lay consultant.

Furthermore, the organization of the Medical Group was less closely adjusted to the round of life of the patient than was that of solo practice. It was less "convenient." The rationalized, cooperative, centralized organization of the Group practice seemed to maximize the full employment of physicians' services while at the same time it seemed to minimize the adjustment of those services to the patients' own perhaps selfish and uninformed but nevertheless subjectively real sense of need for service. Some solo practices (and to some extent the Family Health Maintenance Demonstration during the day) could sustain more waste of professional time and were used simply as a matter of convenience by a fair proportion of patients.

In all, the organization of the Medical Group practice seemed to play a role in the utilization of services in a number of ways. First, the Group organization was such as to impose spatio-temporal barriers to utilization. Where the patient knew of an outside practice that imposed fewer barriers to his convenience, and could absorb the extra cost, he seemed likely to use it. Second, the Group organization imposed cultural or normative barriers to utilization. Where the patient knew of an outside practitioner who would adjust himself to his conception of his illness (or who agreed with his perception), he was likely to use him. And third, the Group organization imposed structural barriers to utilization. When the patient became especially concerned about his illness or problem, he was likely to use an outside practice about which his consultants could give "independent" testimony. In these problems we find illustration for the thesis that there is conflict in the doctor-patient relationship: the patient wants services that conform to his own expectations, not those of professionals.

### The Dilemma of Dependent Practice

Patently, the conceptual distinction between dependent and independent practice parallels the difference between the Montefiore Medical Group and the solo neighborhood practitioner, just as the distinction among types of lay referral system finds some dim reflection in the differences between lower and the upper-middle class patients in The Bronx. By their very abstractness, unclouded by the ambiguity of reality, the analytical distinctions bring into clear focus the dilemma that seems to be central to modern medical practice. If we assume that professionals know and do what is by and large best for their clients, we must conclude that some concrete form of dependent practice in which colleague controls on the quality of care are maximized and patient controls minimized is desirable. However, dependent practice is less likely than independent practice to be satisfactory to the patient. It is more likely to violate his expectations, whether of convenience, sense of interest, or diagnosis and treatment. Being less accommodative, it increases patient resistance. The constraints within it can control the quality of professional services, and can control the patient when he is within it, but they cannot prevent the patient from avoiding those services. If it lacks the advantage of monopoly or special privilege, it may count on treating not the "normal," but largely the desperate, the helpless, and the especially sophisticated.

Thus, dependent practice seems to gain control over professional and client behavior only by giving up the elements that directly attract a clientele. This dilemma would not have any practical importance were it not that the organizational characteristics of dependent practice seem to be emerging as the dominant form of the future. At present dependent practices can rely upon independent practitioners to attract and transmit to them their clientele. In the future the everyday practitioners who are responsible for initially attracting the patient into professional consultation may, like those in the Montefiore Medical Group, work in a milieu that possesses many of the characteristics of dependent practice. The precedent has already been established by the dependent practice of new professions.

## The Rise of Dependent Professions

The distinction between independent and dependent practice may also be used for characterizing professions. An independent profession is one that typically attracts its own clientele. A dependent profession is one that characteristically requires an organization or another profession to attract and transmit to it its clientele. Medicine has been an independent profession. In the distant past it grew up in answer to lay demands. If one was sick, he knew he could go to a surgeon, a barber, a physician, an apothecary, an herb doctor, a blood-stopper, a "barucher," a wart-doctor, or whatever. Easily perceived parts of the body or symptoms each had its specialists, and the patient's knowledge was enough to identify his problem and lead him to the proper specialist. While in some ages it was true that, in Smollett's words, practitioners did "appear in a string, like a flock of wild geese,"[1] the healing practice was not so organized that the patient could not freely exercise choice according to his own prejudices. The world of healing was for him a kind of supermarket in which no single company could monopolize the shelves with its product, and in which each company, lacking subsidy or bulk buyers, depended directly on the individual consumer's choice of its product.

[1] Smollett, Tobias George, *The Adventures of Count Fathom*. Quoted in Turner, Ernest S., *Call The Doctor*. St. Martin's Press, New York, 1959, p. 69.

216        PATIENTS' VIEWS OF MEDICAL PRACTICE

Medicine began to grow by both destroying and absorbing its competitors on the shelves. To do this, of course, it had to forsake its dignity and treat disreputable diseases, overcome its caution and take responsibility for problematic disorders for which patients unreasonably persisted in seeking cure, and cultivate some of the humble but popular skills of its erstwhile rivals. The practices of the bonesetter,[1] the piss-prophet,[2] the clap doctor, and the cataract-gouger[3] in time found their places within medicine as orthopedics, urology, and ophthalmology. Medicine could not extend its domain without absorbing those folk practices, for they served a persistent demand that could not be ignored with impunity. "Dislocated joints," cataracts, venereal disease—these and many other complaints were perceptible however inaccurately, and people sought relief for them. The early medical specialties could be independent, like their folk counterparts, because people could identify them and seek them out for relief.

Some of the newer specialties of medicine, however, were different. They had no analogue in folk practice. They were not wrested away from nonmedical practitioners. No patient would dream of seeking them out himself. They were created by new needs of the medical practitioner himself and were nourished by scientific discovery and the development of an elaborate medical technology. Such specialties as pathology, radiology, and anesthesiology are prime examples. While the patient is involved in what they do, in many ways they may be understood as providing services to other physicians rather than to patients.[4] The patient is often merely instructed to use their services; it is to the physician who referred them rather than to the patient that they

[1] For an informative case history of the conventionalization of folk practice over time, see Joy, Robert J. T., "The Natural Bonesetters with Special Reference to the Sweet Family of Rhode Island: A Study of an Early Phase of Orthopedics," *Bulletin of the History of Medicine*, vol. 28, July–August, 1954, pp. 416–441.

[2] See "Piss-Pot Science," *Journal of the History of Medicine and Allied Sciences*, vol. 10, January, 1955, pp. 121–123. Anonymous.

[3] See Rosen, George, *The Specialization of Medicine with Particular Reference to Ophthalmology*, Froben Press, New York, 1944.

[4] See, for example, how a pioneer anesthesiologist was "hired" by a surgeon. Waters, Ralph M., "Development of Anesthesiology in the U. S. Personal Observations, 1913–1946," *Journal of the History of Medicine and Allied Sciences*, vol. 1, October, 1946, p. 595.

report the outcome of their services. These specialties, which are directly dependent upon colleague referrals or orders for their work, may truly be called dependent or colleague-centered. In them, the relationship between practitioner and client is likely to be qualitatively different from that found in a neighborhood consulting-room.

The development of dependent specialties in medicine runs parallel to a much greater movement in modern society in which are emerging whole professions that may be called dependent. These new dependent professions are being entrusted with increasingly broader responsibilities for the fate of the layman, responsibilities not granted by the layman but by those in positions of authority in the great and complicated political, commercial and service organizations that dominate modern society.

Examples of these dependent professions are found in nursing[1] and in social work. Of the two, it is social work that is the more interesting for our present purposes, since it developed in a larger context, more independently of medicine or any other established profession.[2] Symptomatically, social work rose with the development of great urban aggregates. The masses of people who were attracted or forced into the cities came to suffer difficulties which were new to their experience and for which their traditional remedies were mostly useless—problems of housing, sanitation, employment, transportation, education, and domestic relations. They could not really order their affairs by themselves. In answer to their problems rose a host of new service organizations. After the assistance of lady volunteers was exhausted, new occupations rose to minister to the layman's needs—some civil service positions created by the state, other jobs created by industry and

[1] Nursing is an interesting example. During the nineteenth century its leaders felt obliged to emphasize formal training and deemphasize the reputed gift of the weaker sex for cool hands and compassion. Physicians had no monopoly over cool hands and compassion, but they were beginning to consolidate their monopoly over "scientific" knowledge about healing. Once reputed feminine gifts were denied as adequate credentials for nursing, the only credentials available were those which physicians alone could give. So the nurse became the physician's handmaiden. For a strategic point in the history of nursing, see Woodham-Smith, Cecil, *Florence Nightingale*, McGraw-Hill Book Co., New York, 1951.

[2] For a very useful introduction to the social welfare movement, with an extensive bibliography, see Wilensky, Harold L., and Charles N. Lebeaux, *Industrial Society and Social Welfare*, Russell Sage Foundation, New York, 1958.

commerce, and others nurtured by semi-public service organizations. Social work was one of those new occupations.

Common to all those new occupations was their origin in the way people in policy-making positions perceived the needs of the laymen for whom they had obtained, or were trying to obtain, responsibility. And they were born within the sheltered environment of organizations. In the United States, for example, philanthropic organizations forsook the ancient idea of giving alms for the sake of giving alms and sought instead to give aid only to the worthy poor. They wished to give aid in such a way that it would contribute to the moral well-being of the recipient.[1] One of the roots of social work lay in this problem of discriminating between the worthy and the unworthy, and between useful and wasteful forms of aid. In medicine the early social worker, as almoner, was called upon to distinguish between hospital patients who were entitled to charity care and those who were not; later, to inform physicians in hospitals and clinics about the home conditions of their patients.[2] In all these cases, although she was doing things to and sometimes for the layman, the social worker was doing those things at the request of someone other than the layman. She herself was not sought out for help by the layman. The layman seeking help came to the organization in which she worked, or to other consultants, and was told to use her services. Her practice was founded upon considerations of social policy and organizational or professional requirements, not upon the conscious demands of the client himself.

### Divided Loyalty in Dependent Practice

It is important to the fate of the occupation that it must rely upon others for its clientele. It is equally important to the fate of the client, for practice may develop more than one end, obscuring or compromising the client's "own good." In some cases this is quite obvious. The industrial physician must balance the end of

---

[1] See, for example, Brandt, Lilian, "Growth and Development of New York Association for Improvement of the Condition of the Poor, and Charity Organization Society," Community Service Society, New York, 1942.

[2] A useful document here is Cannon, Ida M., *On the Social Frontier of Medicine*, Harvard University Press, Cambridge, 1952.

industrial production against the patient's welfare when he issues a certificate excusing the "patient" from work.[1] The welfare investigator must balance the rules of eligibility against the client's real need for aid. The military surgeon of the past had to balance the commander's end of punishment against the effects of flogging on the "patient's" health.[2] The employment interviewer must oppose the legal employability of his housewife "client" to her desire to collect unemployment compensation at home instead of working.[3] Such occupations as these patently violate the client's selfish interests. That violation is for the "common good" allows us to accept it as necessary, but it does not vitiate the fact that there is a direct conflict of interest between client and practitioner created by the aims of the organization for which the practitioner works.

Some dependent occupations, though, are explicitly concerned with helping the individual himself; for example, by restoring the client's health or well-being. In spite of that concern, the character of dependent practice encourages considerable differences between the practitioner's and the client's conception of the problem and its solution, thereby increasing conflict. First, the practitioner's conception of the client's problem does not stem from the client but from those policy-makers who guide the organization. Second, when the practitioner has behind him a professional association that has attempted to develop its own esoteric body of "theory" and knowledge, an additional source, without roots in the lay tradition, exists to form the practitioner's views. In social work, for example, when the client asks for money which he believes will solve his problems, the social worker may perceive "immaturity" and prescribe instead a course of treatment in which the client's "insight" will be cultivated.[4] In earlier decades of this century, money might have been denied

---

[1] See Turner, Ernest S., *op. cit.*, p. 250, and Field, Mark G., *Doctor and Patient in Soviet Russia*, Harvard University Press, Cambridge, 1957, pp. 146–180.

[2] Turner, Ernest S., *op. cit.*, p. 92.

[3] See Blau, Peter M., *The Dynamics of Bureaucracy*, University of Chicago Press, Chicago, 1955, pp. 23, 82–83.

[4] The likelihood of this occurring is indicated in Blenkner, Margaret, J. McV. Hunt, and L. S. Kogan, "A Study of Interrelated Factors in the Initial Interview with New Clients," *Social Casework*, vol. 32, 1951, pp. 23–30.

because it seemed unlikely that the client would use it in ways considered beneficial to him.

Intensifying differences between practitioner and client is the very fact of giving services within the framework of an organization. While there is neither logical nor factual basis for assuming that professionals working in a bureaucratic setting must necessarily lose autonomy over the most important aspect of their schooled judgment, working with others will influence the way they do their work. The organization itself is likely to press for the administrative convenience, indeed sometimes necessity, of standardized procedures—eligibility rules, intake forms, referral channels, diagnostic categories, standard therapeutic procedures, and the like. Even though a professional may have sufficient authority to flout them occasionally, those standard procedures are bound to limit his behavior in such a way that he is either reluctant to, or simply cannot, accommodate himself to some of the client's desires.

Perhaps more important than administrative procedures, however, is the constant pressure of colleagues and other fellow-workers to defend their rights against the pressure of both administration and client. What constitutes a fair day's work, or professionally dignified work, what can be rightly demanded of the practitioner—these are assertions of rights, even though they may be rationalized by reference to therapeutic procedure.[1] Supported by patronizing anecdotes about ignorant clients that have the net effect of discounting the client as an informant, and by indignant stories of outrageous demands that have the net effect of discounting the justice of client demands as such,[2] they are a potent source of resistance to him. Both organizational and professional convenience are likely to be given precedence over the client's convenience.

Under the circumstances, the relationship between the dependent practitioner and his client is likely to have to be something like that holding between the parent and the adolescent

[1] This is most graphically illustrated in a forthcoming work by Julius A. Roth.

[2] See Blau, Peter M., *op. cit.*, pp. 88–95, for a discussion of the phenomenon. And see "Bureaucratic Structure and Personality" in Merton, Robert K., *Social Theory and Social Structure* (The Free Press, Glencoe, Ill., 1949, p. 156) for discussion of how personnel may defend their entrenched interests rather than assist the clientele.

child, one asserting that he knows what is for the good of the other (sometimes masking his own self-interest thereby), the other asserting sincerely albeit ignorantly that he knows what is good for himself. Like parent-child conflict, the outcome seems to be determined more by constraint than by communication and understanding. For the new dependent professions this constraint is supplied by the economic and/or political authority supporting the practitioner and, perhaps most importantly, by the likelihood that most other alternatives for help have already been explored unsuccessfully by the client.

The critical problem of the dependent profession occurs when it seeks to become independent—to attract its own clientele. Its problem is even more severe when it tries to attract clients in the early, everyday stage of seeking help, and when it tries to practice preventively. In a limited way, the difficulties of conversion to independent practice were illustrated by the plight of the social workers in the Family Health Maintenance Demonstration. I have suggested that successful conversion seems to require redefinitions of illness as such and relocation of consultation so as to make practice compatible with the lay referral system in which it has no choice but to exist.

## Changing Everyday Practice in Medicine

Superficially, medicine has no such problem. In the United States it has a virtual monopoly on the practice of physical healing, both in fact and in the public imagination. The public wants to be free of what it believes to be physical illness and knows that it is the physician who can treat those ills. Therefore, medicine has firm roots in lay demand, and the everyday practitioner need not be dependent upon anyone else for a clientele. In this he is potentially "independent" still, but increasingly he cannot treat his clientele by modern standards without the help of others. Many of the attributes associated with independent practice are disappearing from medicine: medicine may be facing the problem of satisfying lay demand and attracting a clientele as it shifts from independent practice to a form resembling dependent practice.

The development of clinical knowledge and medical technology has, in many cases, made the patient's understandings irrelevant to diagnosis. As Péquignot has observed,[1] formerly the physician had to take the patient's word for illness, probing the patient's report of his symptoms as well as the outer boundaries of his body. Now, diagnostic procedures can penetrate to the very center of the body and its processes, and yield evidence that makes the patient's subjective feeling and reports superfluous and embarrassing. Increasingly, the problem is to treat someone who does not feel sick or to fail to find anything "objectively" wrong with someone who does feel sick. The patient is less and less equipped to determine to the physician's satisfaction when he is sick and, if so, what sickness it is and so which doctor to see. The two share fewer and fewer diagnostic criteria for illness.

This is itself enough to widen the gap between physician and patient, but there have also been changes in the organization of practice that are extending that gap to a chasm. In the United States, practice without privilege to follow patients into hospitals becomes increasingly difficult and marginal. Everywhere, effective everyday practice has required use of and cooperation with hospitals, laboratories, and special consultants. Practice can no longer be carried on within the confines of the consulting-room, subject only to the patient's scrutiny and the pressure of gossip between the patient and his lay consultants. It becomes dependent upon, and at least partly observable by, colleagues and other medical workers and so becomes at least partly subject to the pressure of those outside standards.[2] Medical practice meeting modern standards can no longer be completely independent, no longer completely client-centered even if it wanted to.

Furthermore, solo practice itself seems, in the United States at least, to be slowly ebbing away. Simple partnerships seem to be becoming increasingly common, and while they are considerably less widespread, medical groups continue to grow and attract the

[1] Péquignot, Henri, "Scientific and Social Aspects of Modern Medicine," *Impact*, vol. 5, December, 1954, pp. 208–210.
[2] Alan Gregg in *Challenges to Contemporary Medicine* (Columbia University Press, New York, 1956, p. 60) indicates that even the presence of a nurse, let alone another physician, tends to raise the level of a physician's performance.

close attention of medical policy-makers. The medical group, said to involve "the application of medical service by a number of physicians working in systematic association with the joint use of equipment and technical personnel and with centralized administration and financial organization"[1] is coming to be the symbol of, if not the norm for, modern scientific medicine. It is often singled out for attention because of the quality of medical care it is supposed to be able to provide.[2] Serving as a centralized point for the organization of varied specialties represented by men who are potentially in daily interaction with each other,[3] and ordered by administrative devices that allow the practitioner time for leisure and study, it does seem plausible that the medical group arrangement will stimulate the physician to provide up-to-date medical care. If quality is not brilliant, then it is likely at least to be more uniform and more predictable than we might expect from a random assortment of solo practitioners.

However, our data suggest that the very organization that makes for high technical quality seems likely also to make for a situation that is less personally satisfactory for the patient. Rudimentarily in simple partnerships and more forcefully in larger cooperative organizations, the day-to-day influence of colleagues on the work of individual practitioners is intensified and the potential influence of the patient weakened. Simply when physicians share their work, "covering" for each other on night and emergency calls, and on vacations or other absences, their relation to their patients is likely to become somewhat more superficial than would be the case if they each were fully responsible to a distinct clientele. Superficiality of commitment is likely to be increased when, with increasing size and efficiency of organiza-

[1] A definition of the House of Delegates of the American Medical Association, December 1, 1948, quoted in Jordan, Edwin P., editor, *The Physician and Group Practice*, Year Book Publishers, Inc., Chicago, 1958, p. 20. See pp. 20–32 for statements of the "principal forms of group practice."

[2] See the compilation of the principal advantages and disadvantages claimed for group practice in Hunt, G. Halsey, "Medical Group Practice in the United States, I. Introduction," *New England Journal of Medicine*, vol. 237, 1947, pp. 71–77.

[3] The actual communication that takes place among colleagues in a medical group can be exaggerated. Joseph Axelrod in "Administrative Aspects of Prepaid Medical Group Practice" (unpublished M.S. thesis, School of Public Health, Yale University School of Medicine, 1951, pp. 50–52) mentions difficulties in establishing communication between family doctors and specialists.

tions of practice, physicians with the same formal qualifications become interchangeable and the patient ceases to be an individual's continuing responsibility. Without a continuing relationship with a particular physician whom he has come to know and to whom he has learned to make effective personal appeals, the patient has lost an important source of leverage in his dealings with doctors.[1] The detachment that is supposed to be appropriate for the doctor's work is supported, but the patient is left with less of a sense of personal interest and less able to influence the course of his management.

It might be argued that the superficiality of the physician's relation with patients under circumstances in which professional controls and standards are emphasized does not really matter so long as the proper diagnostic and therapeutic techniques are used: the patient should certainly have no influence on strictly medical affairs in any case[2] and is better advised to seek gratification for his emotional needs from personal relations outside the consultation room. While this argument may not impress us as very humane or fashionable, it does follow from its assumption of the supreme importance of medical knowledge and technology to patient care. It does not, however, recognize the fact that necessary conditions for the application of knowledge are sociological rather than medical. Patients must be satisfied enough to come in, in the first place, and to cooperate in treatment.

It may be argued reasonably that any lay influence on scientific judgment is to be deplored and is in the long run self-defeating: the price of a little dissatisfaction is well worth the opportunity of insulating one from the other; the patient who is "really" sick will come in anyway. We may agree that some constraints on the patient are necessary and truly in his own interest. In the face of scarce professional skills, visits by appoint-

[1] See the discussion of this as well as a number of other relevant points in the important paper, "The Professional Role of the Physician in Bureaucratized Medicine: A Study in Role Conflict" by J. Ben-David, *Human Relations*, vol. 11, 1958, pp. 255–274.

[2] It might be useful to see this problem in the more general context provided in Bendix, Reinhard, "Bureaucracy: The Problem and Its Setting," *American Sociological Review*, vol. 12, October, 1947, pp. 502–507. The problem of *professional* behavior adds a much more complex dimension to Bendix's discussion.

ment only, tight schedules of being on call for emergency and home visits, priorities for scheduling laboratory procedures, and the like all seem at least partly justified. But as medicine comes to assume the characteristics of dependent practice, apparently medically functional constraints are extended into areas that have no necessary relation to the technical quality of care at all.[1] The very cooperative organization that stimulates the development of professional control of the quality of technical care also stimulates the development of unprecedented professional control of the client.

Some of these new constraints are founded on what are essentially rules of etiquette. Interestingly, they seem to be the ones that the profession has always wished the patient would follow but that, by and large, it has until now been unable to enforce. One previously unenforceable rule states that the patient should not himself consult another doctor for his medical opinion while he is under the care of the one he initially consulted: an additional opinion should be sought only through the doctor who has been treating the patient. Another rule states that the patient should not seek specialist care himself, but should ask his attending physician to refer him: he should go through channels. Both of these rules seek to reduce unwitting competition by sustaining a professionally controlled structure of relationships among physicians. While their enforcement may limit some small waste of scarce professional time, and while it is conceivable that under some circumstances the patient may do himself harm, it is not at all self-evident that these rules are medically, fully justified. Whatever else, they extend professional control over the terms of work and reduce the patient's freedom of activity in seeking help. And it would seem obvious that practice within an organization is much better able to enforce those rules than is solo practice.

Those rules may be embodied—as they are in the Montefiore Medical Group—in the officially stated regulations of the organization. Other rules, however, not necessarily officially stated or

---

[1] See how considerations of "safety" screened extensions of management control over workers in a gypsum plant in Gouldner, Alvin W., *Patterns of Industrial Bureaucracy*, The Free Press, Glencoe, Ill., 1954, p. 198.

even officially recognized may be as important to the fate of the patient. In most organizations these informal norms, developed and sustained by people who work together, focus on definitions of work and on the people and organizations connected with that work.[1] Norms of work tend to distinguish between what is good and desirable and what lowly and undesirable among the activities that the worker may be called upon to perform. And they tend to define what is a fair day's work and its limits, what kind of work is "really" necessary for the performance of a task, and, of course, what is fair compensation. Norms about personnel tend to involve a definition of the relation of the administration and its representatives to the worker, to distinguish between the lowly and the high, the lazy and the dangerously energetic among fellow-workers, and the "good" and "bad" clients. They define, in short, the stance the worker takes toward those events, people, and pressures that both constitute and interrupt the orderly and convenient routine of a fair and reasonable day's work. While they cannot be completely separated from the question of technical standards, it is certain that, whatever else, they involve professional conceptions of working conditions. Those social standards are often disguised as, and confounded with, technical medical standards, and given the same sacrosanct position.[2] They can better solidify and be enforced in an organization than in practice by isolated individuals.

### The Future of the Patient

The argument can be summarized as follows. Modern medicine still has roots in client demand, as it had in the past. Lately, however, it has become more and more dependent upon a varied array of colleagues and medical organizations which stand outside the lay community that the practice serves. This much is certain about present-day trends in medicine, and since practice is becoming subject to that external pressure in the course of

[1] The outstanding statement of these informal norms is to be found in the work of Everett C. Hughes.

[2] Mention of the forthcoming work of Julius A. Roth is again in order as an explicit statement of how work rules in hospitals are often disguised as or falsely justified by reference to the science underlying medicine.

becoming dependent upon it, it follows that medical culture becomes more and more insulated from patient culture; the amount of control that the patient can exercise over his fate in the consulting-room is being reduced.

In addition, though it is by no means a certain trend at this date, it appears that everyday practice is moving away from the solitary entrepreneurial form toward some sort of cooperative, organized form, of which the Montefiore Medical Group is an example. If this is true, and if what sociologists have already learned about factories, business firms, armies, hospitals, schools, and prisons is also true of medical groups, it follows that the net of constraints surrounding the patient is being tightened further. Some of these constraints may be justified by the fact that they are essential to allowing and encouraging the physician to practice a high quality of medicine. This is probably not true of all such constraints, however, for some, supported by the same organization that allows the development of higher technical standards, are likely merely to serve the convenience of the practitioner and increase his control of the *terms* of his work without any necessary relation to the *quality* of his work.

What is the future of the patient, then, assuming that the patient cannot adjust himself or be adjusted to practice without some change in the practice as well? If the future involves the sort of care that is provided at the Montefiore Medical Group, the potentialities are very great indeed, for with able and conscientious physicians, strong professional controls, and systematic administrative procedures, care of a high technical quality is as predictable as human efforts can make it.[1] This high quality, however, seems dependent for its maintenance upon circumstances which by supporting the physician's ability to practice "good" medicine also impose a great many restrictions on the patient's convenience, on the mode by which he seeks care, and on the manner by which he can convince himself of its adequacy.

[1] In unpublished reports by eminent outside consultants who have made extensive study of samples of medical records, high praise is expressed for the technical quality of the medical care practiced in the Montefiore Medical Group. And see the comments about the Group in Fox, T. F., "The Personal Doctor and His Relation to the Hospital," *The Lancet*, no. 7127, April 2, 1960, pp. 743–760.

In doing so, it is at least partly self-defeating. While no very great proportion of patients expressed extreme dissatisfaction with the Montefiore Medical Group, a fair proportion expressed attitudes testifying to a kind of uneasiness, an irritability, a sense of something lacking. We could not determine directly the relationship between those vague attitudes of discontent and the *quality* of utilization of services and of cooperation in treatment, but it does seem reasonable to think that utilization will not be optimal and cooperation will not be all it can be when the patient feels helpless and at the mercy of professional judgment and interest. This may be particularly the case when there is no "outside" practice to serve the function of a safety-valve and when medical groups provide no definite channels for complaint and redress.

If this is true, some resolution of the problem seems necessary before all the potentialities of modern medical care can be realized. What can be done to make practice better able to gain the kind of patient cooperation that exploits fully the resources of medicine? Much of the emphasis today is on medical education— teaching future doctors to understand more fully the sociological and psychological factors involved in illness and patient behavior. This is sound enough, but it cannot be presumed that schooled understanding will be put to work no matter what the situation in which the physician must work. If the proportion of physicians in the United States does not increase—and it would seem that the best one can hope for now is maintaining the present proportion—it is unlikely that a situation will exist in which that new enlightenment can be applied satisfactorily. Indeed, I suspect that it is the quantitative pressure of patients as much as if not more than the complexity of medical knowledge and technology that is responsible for the growth in the United States of cooperative forms of practice which can handle more patients and still guarantee the physician some leisure time.

Beyond medical education, therefore, it would seem necessary to deal with the way the physician is to practice. Empirical study of present forms of practice is desperately needed, for at present we have no adequate foundation of systematic knowledge about any kind of medical practice. Careful study should uncover numerous areas of physician behavior that dissatisfy and discourage patients and so interfere with the presumed end of good and successful patient care. Some are certain to be unnecessary for a high quality of technical care; supported by professional rationalizations, sustaining an occupational position but working against the end by which the occupation's existence is justified. Unlike technical standards, these are negotiable and might be subject to experimentation.

The mere mention of "experimentation" with physicians, however, is likely to occasion the amusement or indignation that is fitting commentary on what is practical and what is not. Like other established professions, the physician has kicked himself upstairs into a largely supervisory capacity that is too remote, too entrenched, and above all too scarce to have to tolerate experimentation. It is for this reason that I believe that the best practical hope for the future lies in obtaining the physician's cooperation and aid in experimenting with new therapeutic roles. As the nurse was used in the Family Health Maintenance Demonstration, so she or some entirely new profession might be moved into the vacuum left by the withdrawal of the physician from the day-to-day, highly accessible, advice-giving role which finds a natural place in the lay referral system.

It is a common process for lesser occupations to move into the vacuum left by the upward mobility of others, as Hughes has observed at some length,[1] but in medicine this process has been hampered by professional insistence on sole legal jurisdiction even over areas of practice which are increasingly avoided by physicians as too minor, unpleasant, or undignified to be worth dealing with. General practice itself is being avoided. In hospitals and in backward areas of the world healing has been practiced by nonphysicians. There have existed for some time the assistant, the *feldsher*, and other sorts of lesser medical practitioner. It might well be time in the United States to consider establishing "subsidiary" professions in everyday practice that set roots down into

[1] See particularly Hughes, E. C., H. M. Hughes, and I. Deutscher, *Twenty Thousand Nurses Tell Their Story*, J. B. Lippincott Co., Philadelphia, 1958.

unfulfilled client demand, using limited authority to give medical advice, to diagnose, to prescribe drugs, to administer treatment and, where necessary, to refer the patient to physicians.[1] Standing between the physician and the patient, this role will share its difficulties with all middle-man roles, but it is an obvious means of bridging the growing chasm between the doctor and the patient. The Family Health Maintenance Demonstration contained particularly instructive examples of both the difficulties in and the possibilities of accomplishing it.

If the future sees the patient more helpless, and the foundation of medical practice so systematically closed that no "outside" accommodating practices remain, perhaps, as Péquignot suggests he has already done, the patient may take flight into magic.[2] More likely he will continue to get along but will present the evasive, resentful but desperately demanding face to the medical world that all people present when confronted by forces they cannot control, which they know are sometimes indifferent to them, but which they cannot do without.

[1] See the discussion in Hollingshead, August B., and Frederick C. Redlich, *Social Class and Mental Illness*, John Wiley and Sons, New York, pp. 377–378.

[2] Péquignot, Henri, *op. cit.*, pp. 235–237.

# APPENDIX

# FAMILY HEALTH MAINTENANCE DEMONSTRATION
## QUESTIONNAIRE

### (Number 1)

## INSTRUCTIONS

This questionnaire has been designed to determine
how the organization of the Family Health program
has worked for you. It is short and shouldn't
take more than a few minutes of your time.

Note that there are two columns to fill in, one
for the husband and one for the wife. If both
cannot fill in their columns, it is most important
that the WIFE fill in hers.

In filling out the questionnaire, try to answer
every question, even though you may feel your
answer is very arbitrary. We want a GENERAL picture of your experience over the WHOLE TIME you
have been on the program, not just your experience
of the recent past.

It may help you to know that the PUBLIC HEALTH
NURSES of the program have been Miss − − − − − and
Miss − − − − −, the SOCIAL WORKERS have been
Miss − − − − −, Mrs. − − − − − and Miss − − − − −,
the SECRETARIES have been Mrs. − − − − − −,
Mrs. − − − − −, Miss − − − − − and Mrs. − − − − −,
and the DOCTORS and PEDIATRICIANS have been
Drs. − − − − −, − − − − − −, − − − − − −, − − − − −
and − − − − −.

Your name is needed on this questionnaire only as
a check on returns. After your name is checked,
your answers will be tabulated without reference
to your identity.

# QUESTIONNAIRE FOR FAMILY HEALTH PATIENTS

Name_____

Husband's Occupation_____

_____

\*\*\*\*\*\*\*\*\*\*\*\*\*\*\*\*\*\*\*\*\*\*\*\*\*\*\*\*\*\*\*

READ EACH QUESTION THROUGH COMPLETELY BEFORE ANSWERING.

1. To whom have you made the greatest number of office visits for which you made an advance appointment?

   Using your general recollection of all the years you've been in Family Health, write a "1" beside the person you've seen most by appointment, "2" beside the one you've seen next most often, and so on to "3" beside the person you've seen least or not at all by appointment.

   Husband Wife

   _____ _____ Public Health Nurse

   _____ _____ Doctor or Pediatrician

   _____ _____ Social Worker

2. Whom have you called on the phone for one thing or another?

   Using your general recollection of all the years you've been in Family Health, write a "1" beside the person you've called the most, "2" beside the one you've called almost as much, and so on to "4" for the one you've called least or not at all.

Husband Wife

_____ _____ Doctor or Pediatrician

_____ _____ Social Worker

_____ _____ Public Health Nurse

_____ _____ Secretary (to talk to her, not to ask her to contact someone else for you).

3. With whom in Family Health have you had the greatest number of informal chats about your affairs, chats not scheduled by appointment?

   Using your general recollection of all the years you've been in Family Health, write a "1" beside the person you've chatted with most, and so on to "4" beside the person you've chatted with least or not at all.

   Husband Wife

   _____ _____ Secretary

   _____ _____ Public Health Nurse

   _____ _____ Social Worker

   _____ _____ Pediatrician or Doctor

4. If you or some member of your family had some tests or x-rays, whom would you be most likely to try to reach at Family Health to tell you the results and interpret them for you? CHECK that ONE person.

Husband Wife

_____ _____ Doctor or Pediatrician

_____ _____ Social Worker

_____ _____ Public Health Nurse

5. If you couldn't get that person you checked above, and didn't want to wait, whom would you be most likely to try to reach instead to tell you the results and interpret them for you? CHECK that ONE person.

Husband Wife

_____ _____ Social Worker

_____ _____ Doctor or Pediatrician

_____ _____ Public Health Nurse

_____ _____ Secretary

6. If someone in your family had a cold too minor for a home-call or for coming in to Family Health, but you wanted to be sure you were doing the best you could, whom would you call for advice?

Mark a "1" beside the person you'd be most likely to call, a "2" beside the next most likely, and so on to "5" beside the person you'd be least likely to call.

Husband Wife

_____ _____ Public Health Nurse

_____ _____ Social Worker

_____ _____ Secretary (for her to choose the right person for you).

_____ _____ Doctor or Pediatrician

_____ _____ Secretary (for her advice about handling the problem).

7. If you were having a problem getting your child to go to bed, whom would you call for advice at Family Health?

Mark a "1" beside the person you'd be most likely to call, a "2" beside the next most likely, and so on to "5" beside the person you'd be least likely to call for advice.

Husband Wife

_____ _____ Secretary (for her to choose the right person for you).

_____ _____ Public Health Nurse

_____ _____ Social Worker

_____ _____ Secretary (for her advice about handling the problem).

_____ _____ Doctor or Pediatrician

8. If you were having a problem getting one of the
children to eat, whom
would you call for advice
at Family Health?

Write a "1" beside the
person you'd be <u>most</u>
likely to call, and so on
to "5" beside the person
you'd be <u>least</u> likely to
call for advice.

Husband <u>Wife</u>

———— ——— Social Worker

———— ——— Secretary
(for her
advice about
handling the
problem).

———— ——— Doctor or
Pediatrician

———— ——— Public Health
Nurse

———— ——— Secretary
(for her to
choose the
right person
for you).

9. If you were having a
school problem with one of
your children, whom would
you call for advice at
Family Health?

Write a "1" beside the
person you'd be <u>most</u>
likely to call, "2" beside
the person you'd be less
likely to call, and so on
to "5" beside the person
you'd be <u>least</u> likely to
call for advice.

Husband <u>Wife</u>

———— ——— Doctor or
Pediatrician

———— ——— Public Health
Nurse

———— ——— Secretary
(for her to
choose the
right person
for you).

———— ——— Social Worker

———— ——— Secretary
(for her
advice about
handling the
problem).

10. Family Health is different from HIP in many
ways. We'd like to learn
what differences have
been most important
<u>to you.</u>

a. Below is a list of some
of the technical differ-
ences. Mark the one that
has been <u>most important</u>
<u>to you</u> with a "1," the
next most important with
a "2," and so on to the
<u>least important</u> with a
"5."

Husband <u>Wife</u>

———— ——— Being able
to get
appointments
quickly.

———— ——— Dental care
for the
children.

———— ——— Greater num-
ber of
routine med-
ical tests.

———— ——— Calling you
for the
annual phys-
ical exam.

———— ——— Easier to
see someone
without an
appointment.

b. Below is a list of some
   of the differences in
   personnel.  Mark the most
   important with a "1" and
   so on to the least im-
   portant with a "4."

   Husband Wife

   _____  ____  Having
                    Social
                    Workers.

   _____  ____  Having doc-
                    tors who can
                    spend more
                    time with
                    you than
                    they can in
                    regular HIP.

   _____  ____  Having
                    special
                    secretaries.

   _____  ____  Having Pub-
                    lic Health
                    Nurses.

USE THIS SPACE FOR ANY
COMMENTS YOU MIGHT HAVE ON
YOUR ANSWERS.

AS SOON AS YOU'VE FILLED OUT
THE QUESTIONNAIRE, PLEASE
PUT IT IN ENCLOSED ENVELOPE
AND MAIL IMMEDIATELY.

FAMILY HEALTH MAINTENANCE DEMONSTRATION
QUESTIONNAIRE

(Number 2)

## INSTRUCTIONS

Most of the questions in this questionnaire can be
answered by placing a checkmark beside the item
you agree with.  In a few cases, though, you will
find different instructions.  Please read those
special instructions carefully before answering
the questions.

Your answers to this questionnaire will be pooled
with those of other patients and not identified
with your name.  In fact, your name is necessary
only to allow us to check on returns.

Note that your answers will have no effect on anyone's job in the Demonstration, for the Demonstration is an experiment that cannot be changed for
the whole of its duration.  However, your answers
will have some effect on plans for changing the
regular HIP program of medical care at Montefiore.
Therefore, complete frankness would be most useful, and will harm no one.

Note that two questionnaires are enclosed, both
almost identical.  One should be filled out by the
husband and the other by the wife.  It is very
important that BOTH questionnaires be filled out
and MAILED BACK AS SOON AS POSSIBLE.  A stamped
return envelope is enclosed for your convenience.

Thank you.

# FAMILY HEALTH MAINTENANCE DEMONSTRATION
## WIFE'S QUESTIONNAIRE

Name_____

Occupation_____

If housewife, former occupation_____

\*\*\*\*\*\*\*\*\*\*\*\*\*\*\*\*\*\*\*\*\*\*\*\*\*\*\*\*\*\*\*

1. On the whole, have you liked being a member of the Demonstration?

    ____Yes

    ____No

2. Do you think you've gotten better medical care in Family Health than you got when you were in regular HIP?

    ____Yes, better than regular HIP

    ____No, worse than regular HIP

    ____About the same

3. Do you think you've gotten better medical care in Family Health than you got from private doctors before you had HIP?

    ____Yes, better than private doctors

    ____No, worse than private doctors

    ____About the same

4. Do you think you've gotten better medical care in regular HIP than you've gotten from private doctors?

    ____Better than private doctors

    ____Worse than private doctors

    ____About the same

5. Check the one most important thing about the kind of medical care you've gotten in Family Health that you feel you have not gotten in regular HIP.

    ____Enough tests and examinations

    ____Really good doctors

    ____Personal interest

    ____Other (Write in):_____

    _____

    _____

6. Check the one most important thing about the kind of medical care you've gotten in Family Health that you feel you have not gotten enough of from private practice.

    ____Enough tests and examinations

    ____Really good doctors

    ____Personal interest

    ____Other (Write in):_____

    _____

7. Do you think the Demonstration has uncovered things wrong with you that you didn't know about before?

    ____Yes

    ____No

    ____Don't know

239

8. Do you think the Demonstration has treated you for things that were never treated before?

    ____Yes

    ____No

    ____Don't know

9. Has it ever seemed to be a lot of bother to belong to the Demonstration and have to come in for annual exams and so many other tests?

    ____Yes, a lot of bother

    ____Yes, a little bother

    ____No bother at all

10. Have some of the recommendations made to you by Family Health Personnel ever seemed too hard to follow through, or too much trouble to be worth bothering about? Some recommendations other patients have found difficult are such things as losing weight, having special shots or tests, and trying to relax.

    ____Yes, a few recommendations seemed too hard or too much bother

    ____No, none of the recommendations seemed too hard or too much of a bother to follow through

*******************************

11. Do you think you've made more use of the Pediatrician and the Family Doctor of the Demonstration than you made of the doctors you had while a regular HIP subscriber downstairs?

    ____Yes, a lot more

    ____Yes, a little more

    ____About the same

    ____No, less

12. Using your general recollection of all the years you've been in Family Health, write a "1" beside the person you feel you've used most often, a "2" beside the person used next most often, a "3" beside the person used next most often, and a "4" beside the person you've used least.

    ____Family Doctor (Drs.——— or ———)

    ____Pediatrician (Drs.———, ——— or ———)

    ____Public Health Nurse (Miss _____ or Mrs. ———)

    ____Social Worker (Mrs.———, Miss ——— or Miss———)

13. Using your recollection of all the years you've been in Family Health, write a "1" beside the person you've felt most friendly with, a "2" beside the person you've felt next most friendly with, a "3" beside the person you feel is next, and a "4" beside the person you've felt least friendly with. See names above

    ____Family Doctor

    ____Pediatrician

    ____Public Health Nurse

    ____Social Worker

14. While you've been in Family Health, have you come in to see the doctor when you had just a cold?

____Yes, occasionally

____No, never

15. How about calling—have you called the doctor on the phone for advice when you had just a cold?

____Yes, occasionally

____No, never

16. If you should be having trouble getting along with people, or difficulties in your marriage, do you feel there's anyone at Family Health you can get advice from?

____Yes

____No

____Don't know

17. Let's say you had such trouble and you had nowhere to turn for help but to Family Health. Write a "1" beside the person you'd be most likely to ask for help or advice, a "2" beside the person you'd be next most likely to ask, a "3" beside the person you'd be next most likely to ask, and a "4" beside the person you'd be least likely to ask.

____Family Doctor

____Pediatrician

____Public Health Nurse

____Social Worker

****************************

The Demonstration has provided you with the services of a Public Health Nurse and of a Social Worker. These services are not ordinarily given in HIP. Besides these extra services, the Family Doctor and the Pediatrician have a bit more time to spend with you than doctors usually have in regular HIP. The question is, which of these two extras is most important to you? Your answer will help plan possible changes in regular HIP care and will not affect the current situation in Family Health.

18. If you had to make a choice, which of the below would you choose? Check one.

____More important to have a family doctor and pediatrician who can spend as much time with me as they now do in Family Health, even if having that extra time means getting along without the services of a public health nurse or social worker.

____More important to have the services of a public health nurse or a social worker, even if having those extra services means having only as much time with the doctor and pediatrician as one usually has in regular HIP.

____Makes no difference which is chosen.

19. No matter what you answered above, if it were
necessary to choose be-
tween having the services
of a public health nurse
like Miss ———— or Mrs.
———— and the services
of a social worker like
Mrs. ———— or Miss
————, how would you
choose?  Make your choice
on the basis of your own
needs and past ex-
perience.

____If I couldn't have
both, would prefer
having a social
worker.

____If I couldn't have
both, would prefer
having a public health
nurse.

____Makes no difference
which one.

****************************

Now, a few questions about
your use of private health
services.  In your answers,
ignore the occasions when you
were out of town and could
not get HIP care.

20. Before you were in Family
Health and when you were
a regular HIP subscriber,
did you or any member of
your family eligible for
HIP care ever have a
surgical operation (or
child delivery) performed
by a private medical
doctor?

____Yes, at our own
expense

____Yes, on Blue Shield,
to which we also
belong

____No, never

21. If you answered "yes,"
check the family members
who had such operations.

____Husband

____Wife

____Children up to 6 years
old

____Children 6 years old
and over

____Other (Write in):____
_____

22. Excluding operations now,
before you were in Family
Health, when you were a
regular HIP subscriber,
did you or any member of
your family eligible for
HIP care use the services
of a private doctor?

____Yes, quite a bit

____Yes, occasionally

____No, never

23. If you answered "yes,"
check the family members
who used such private
services.

____Husband

____Wife

____Children up to 6 years
old

____Children 6 years old
and over

____Other (Write in):____
_____

24. While you've been in
Family Health, did you or
any eligible member of
your family have a
surgical operation (or
child delivery) performed
by a private doctor?

____Yes, at our own
expense

____Yes, on Blue Shield

____No

25. Excluding operations now, while you've been in Family Health, did you or any eligible member of your family use the services of a private doctor?

____Yes, quite a bit

____Yes, occasionally

____No

Finally, since we're concerned with you as a family member, we'd like a little information about that.

26. How long have you lived in your present neighborhood?

____Less than a year

____1–3 years

____3–6 years

____6 years and more

27. Do your parents (not in-laws) live close by you?

____Yes, at least one

____No, none (or deceased)

28. Do any other relatives, such as brothers or sisters, in-laws, grandparents, aunts or uncles live close by you?

____Yes, some or all

____No, none

29. How often do you see your parents or parents-in-law?

____I see some (one or more) of them very often––at least once a week

____I never see any of them more than occasionally––once a month or so

____I don't see any of them very much (or deceased)

30. How often do you see other relatives, such as brothers, sisters, grandparents, aunts and uncles?

____I see some (one or more) of them very often––at least once a week

____I never see any of them more than occasionally––once a month or so

____I never see any of them very much

31. Do any really close friends of yours live close by?

____Yes

____No

32. How often do you see your really close friends?

____I see some (one or more) of them very often––at least once a week

____I never see any of them more than occasionally––once a month or so

____I never see any of them very much

*****************************

THIS IS THE END OF THE QUESTIONNAIRE. THANK YOU FOR FILLING IT OUT. NOW, PLEASE PUT THIS AND THE QUESTIONNAIRE OF YOUR HUSBAND OR WIFE INTO RETURN ENVELOPE AND MAIL BACK TO US.

*****************************

# FAMILY HEALTH MAINTENANCE DEMONSTRATION
## FINAL HUSBAND'S QUESTIONNAIRE
### (Number 3)

Name_____

IBM columns 1-10

11. Do you think you and your family are in better health now than you were before entering Family Health?

____Yes, most of us probably better.

____No, most of us about the same.

____No, most of us probably worse.

____Don't know.

12. Do you think that Family Health had much to do with the general health of you and your family?

____Yes, it improved our health.

____While it hasn't improved it, it has prevented our health from becoming bad or getting worse.

____No, had little effect.

____Made our health worse.

____Don't know.

13. How do you feel Family Health compares with regular Montefiore HIP care in its effect on the general health of you and your family?

____More likely to be healthy as a Family Health patient.

____More likely to be healthy as a regular HIP patient.

____Probably makes no difference one way or another.

14. How do you feel Family Health compares with the private medical care you have had in its effect on the general health of you and your family?

____More likely to be healthy as a patient of a private doctor.

____More likely to be healthy as a Family Health patient.

____Probably makes no difference one way or another.

15. How do you feel regular Montefiore HIP medical care compares with the private medical care you have had in its effect on the general health of you and your family?

____More likely to be healthy as a patient of a private doctor.

____More likely to be healthy as a regular Montefiore HIP patient.

____Probably makes no difference one way or another.

244

16. Most of you seem to have found it pleasant to be a patient in the Family Health Maintenance Demonstration. How does the Demonstration compare in pleasantness with regular Montefiore HIP care?

____More pleasant to be a regular HIP patient.

____More pleasant to be a Family Health patient.

____About as pleasant to be a regular HIP patient as to be a Family Health patient.

17. How does the Demonstration compare in pleasantness with the private medical care you have had?

____More pleasant to be the patient of a private doctor.

____More pleasant to be a Family Health patient.

____About as pleasant to be the patient of a private doctor as to be a Family Health patient.

18. How does regular Montefiore HIP compare in pleasantness with the private medical care you have had?

____More pleasant to be a regular HIP patient.

____More pleasant to be the patient of a private doctor.

____About as pleasant to be a regular HIP patient as to be a private patient.

Family Health provided you with the services of a Public Health Nurse and of a Social Worker. These services are not ordinarily given in HIP. Besides these extra services, the Family Health doctors had a bit more time to spend with you than HIP doctors usually have. Which of these two extras is most important to you now that you have left the FHMD?

19. If you had to make a choice, which of the below would you choose? Check one.

____More important to have doctors who can spend as much time with me as they did in Family Health, even if having that extra time means getting along without a public health nurse or social worker.

____More important to have the services of a public health nurse or a social worker, even if that means having only as much time with the doctors as one usually has in regular HIP.

____Makes no difference which is chosen.

20. No matter what you answered above, if it were necessary to choose between having the services of a public health nurse like Miss————— or Mrs.————— and those of a social worker like Mrs.—————, or Miss—————, how would you choose?

_____If I couldn't have both, would prefer having a social worker.

_____If I couldn't have both, would prefer having a public health nurse.

_____Makes no difference which one.

*******************************

21. How long has it been since you left Family Health?

_____Less than a year.

_____1-2 years.

_____2-3 years.

_____More than 3 years.

22. Do you still belong to HIP?

_____Yes

_____No

If you answered, "No," when did you leave the plan?

_____While a member of Family Health

_____Within a year after leaving FHMD

_____Within 1-2 years after leaving FHMD

_____Within 2-3 years after leaving FHMD

_____More than 3 years after leaving FHMD

23. Please explain why you left HIP.

_____

_____

_____

_____

24. If you still belong to HIP do you also belong to the Montefiore Medical Group now?

_____Yes

_____No

If you answered, "No," when did you leave the Montefiore Medical Group?

_____While a member of Family Health.

_____Within a year after leaving FHMD.

_____1-2 years after leaving FHMD.

_____2-3 years after leaving FHMD.

_____More than 3 years after leaving FHMD

25. Please explain why you left Montefiore Medical Group.

_____

_____

_____

_____

ALL THOSE WHO NO LONGER BELONG TO HIP OR THE MONTE-FIORE MEDICAL GROUP NEED NOT FILL OUT ANY MORE. PLEASE RETURN THE QUESTIONNAIRES IN THE ENCLOSED ENVELOPE.

ALL THOSE WHO STILL BELONG TO HIP AND THE MONTEFIORE MEDICAL GROUP, PLEASE CONTINUE.

26. Do you have the same Family Doctor you had before you became a member of the Family Health Maintenance Demonstration?

_____Yes

_____No

27. Since leaving FHMD, have you ever asked to change your Family Doctor?

____Yes, I've asked to change him.

____No, but I've sometimes wanted to change.

____No, and never wanted to.

28. Do you feel your present Family Doctor takes as much interest in you as he should?

____Yes

____No

____Haven't used him since leaving FHMD.

____Don't know.

29. Do you feel your present HIP pediatrician takes as much interest in your children as he (or she) should?

____Yes

____No

____My children are past the age for a pediatrician, so don't know.

____My children are eligible for a pediatrician, but haven't used him, so don't know.

30. Do you feel the HIP specialists you've seen take as much interest in you as they should?

____Yes

____No

____Haven't used any specialists since FHMD, so can't say.

31. Some people say that the Montefiore Medical Group has a clinic atmosphere that makes them feel they're charity cases. Do you agree?

____Yes, very much.

____Yes, a bit.

____No, not at all.

If you answered, "Yes," did you feel that the Family Health Maintenance Demonstration also had a clinic atmosphere?

____Yes, very much

____Yes, a bit

____No, not at all

32. Since you left Family Health, have you or anyone in your family eligible for HIP care had a surgical operation or a child delivery?

____No

____Yes

If you answered, "Yes," was this operation or child delivery performed by a HIP doctor?

____Yes

____No, but HIP paid for it.

____No, but it was paid for by Blue Shield, or some other surgical plan.

____No, and we paid for it ourselves.

(33-35) If HIP was not used, please write in the nature of the operation

and the reason for not
using HIP.

_____

_____

_____

36. Excluding the above,
    since you left FHMD have
    you or any other member
    of your family eligible
    for HIP ever used the
    services of a non–HIP
    doctor?

    ____No, never used non–HIP
    doctors in the time
    since leaving FHMD.

    ____Yes, since leaving
    FHMD have occasionally
    used a non–HIP doctor,
    but HIP has been used
    for most of our med-
    ical needs.

    ____Yes, use a non–HIP
    doctor for most med-
    ical needs, hardly
    using HIP at all.

37. If you answered, "Yes,"
    which of the following
    characterizes the non–HIP
    doctor you have used? If
    more than one kind of
    doctor was used, please
    double–check the one used
    most.

    ____General practitioner
    (a regular doctor who
    treats many things).

    ____Internist.

    ____Pediatrician (Children
    only).

    ____Gynecologist (Women
    only).

    ____Some other kind of
    specialist.

38. Which of the following
    best describes the prac-
    tice of the non–HIP doc-
    tor you have used? If
    you have used more than
    one kind, please double-
    check the one used most.

    ____An office in my own
    local neighborhood.

    ____An office in my former
    neighborhood.

    ____An office not in my
    neighborhood, but in
    The Bronx.

    ____An office in downtown
    Manhattan.

39. Among the non–HIP doctors
    you used, was one of them
    the regular doctor you
    had before joining HIP?

    ____Yes

    ____No

40. Did you use any of these
    non–HIP doctors while you
    were in the Family Health
    Maintenance Demonstra-
    tion?

    ____Yes

    ____No

41. On the whole, are you
    satisfied with the care
    you've gotten at the
    Montefiore Medical Group
    since you left Family
    Health?

    ____Yes, completely satis-
    fied.

    ____Some complaints, but
    generally satisfied.

    ____No, generally dis-
    satisfied.

42. Here are some things patients have complained
about at the Montefiore
Medical Group.  Please
check the ONE complaint
you feel is justified and
really important.

____No important com-
plaints.

____Waiting for the doctor
even when I have an
appointment.

____Feeling that the doc-
tor's rushing me in
and out of the office.

____Can't keep the same
doctor, they change so
often.

____Can't get house-calls.

____Some other complaint
really important:

_____

_____

_____

_____

43. Do you have any relatives
who are also members of
the Montefiore Medical
Group?

____Yes, many of them are.

____Yes, a few of them
are.

____No, none that I know
of.

44. Does anyone you know at
work belong to the Monte-
fiore Medical Group?

____Yes, many of them do.

____Yes, a few of them do.

____No, none that I know
of.

45. Do you know whether any
of your neighbors belong
to the Montefiore Medical
Group?

____Yes, many of them do.

____Yes, a few of them do.

____No, none that I know
of.

THIS IS THE END OF THE QUESTIONNAIRE. PLEASE RETURN
IT IN THE ENCLOSED ENVELOPE AS SOON AS POSSIBLE.

## MONTEFIORE MEDICAL GROUP QUESTIONNAIRE

### INSTRUCTIONS

This is a survey of a randomly selected sample of subscribers to the Montefiore Medical Group, HIP. It is designed to find out what your experience has been with medical care both in and out of HIP.

Filling out the questionnaire should take little time, since most items can be answered with a check mark or an "X." IT IS IMPORTANT THAT YOU ANSWER EVERY QUESTION YOU CAN. Even if you have made no use of HIP services at all, your answers are important and valuable to us.

Note that it is not necessary for you to write in your name. A number is stamped on the questionnaire so we can check returns and remind those who have forgotten to send in their answers, but once your questionnaire is returned the survey-card that contains your name and code-number will be destroyed. In this way we guarantee that your answers are kept strictly confidential.

For your convenience, a stamped, return envelope is enclosed. When you have filled out the questionnaire, please mail. Do not bring it to the Center — it will be sure to reach the survey only if you mail it back to us in the return envelope. Please mail it back to us as soon as possible.

# MONTEFIORE MEDICAL GROUP QUESTIONNAIRE

FIRST, A FEW QUESTIONS ABOUT YOU

1. Sex

  ____Male

  ____Female

2. Age

  ____15-29 years

  ____30-44 years

  ____45-59 years

  ____60 - and over

3. Marital status

  ____Married

  ____Divorced or separated

  ____Widow or widower

  ____Single, never married

4. Check those in your family eligible for HIP care.

  ____My wife or husband and our children

  ____Only myself and my child

  ____Only my wife or husband and myself

  ____Only myself

  ____Other (Write in):____

  _____

5. Do you have children who have used HIP pediatricians?

  ____Yes

  ____No

6. How many years have you been a subscriber to HIP?

  ____Less than a year

  ____1 - 2 years

  ____3 - 4 years

  ____More than 4 years

NOW SOME QUESTIONS ABOUT WHAT YOU THINK OF HIP

7. When you joined HIP were you sorry to leave your regular non-HIP doctor?

  ____Yes, sorry to leave him

  ____No, because kept him anyway

  ____No, not sorry to leave him

  ____Had no regular doctor before HIP

8. Does it seem to you that on the whole HIP doctors are better doctors than the ones you had before you joined HIP?

  ____Yes, HIP doctors are better

  ____HIP and non-HIP doctors about the same

  ____Non-HIP doctors are better

  ____Don't know

9. Do you think that on the whole you've gotten better medical care from the Montefiore Group than you got from non-HIP doctors before you belonged to HIP?

  ____Yes, got better medical care from Group

  ____No, got better medical care from non-HIP doctors

  ____Medical care from Group and non-HIP doctors was about the same

  ____Don't know

251

10. Does it seem to you that on the whole the doctors in HIP are more interested in you than the doctors you had before you joined HIP?

____Yes, HIP doctors more interested

____HIP and non-HIP doctors are about the same

____No, non-HIP doctors are more interested

____Never used HIP so can't say

11. Have you ever asked to change your HIP Family Doctor?

____Yes, I've asked to change my doctor

____No, but I've sometimes wanted to change

____No, and I never wanted to change

12. Here are some things patients have complained about in HIP. Please check the ONE most important complaint that you agree with.

____Waiting for the doctor even when I have an appointment

____Feeling that the doctor's rushing me in and out the office

____Can't keep the same doctor, they change so often

____Can't get house-calls

____No complaints

____Some other complaint most important:_____
_____
_____

13. Some patients have made some of the same complaints about non-HIP medical practice.

Please check the ONE most important complaint about non-HIP doctors that you agree with.

____Waiting for the doctor even when I have an appointment

____Feeling that the doctor's rushing me in and out the office

____Too expensive

____Can't get house-calls

____No complaints

____Some other complaint most important:_____
_____
_____

14. Most people have a favorite doctor, or a doctor they liked a great deal. Thinking back over the doctors you've known during the past 15 years, which one have you liked best?

____A HIP doctor I had

____A non-HIP doctor I had

____Several favorites both HIP and non-HIP doctors

15. If you had to pick one doctor out of a group, what kind would you choose? Check one answer below.

____The smartest and best doctor, and I wouldn't care too much whether he took personal interest in me or not

____The best personality,
the one who'd take the
most personal interest
in me

____Other (Write in):____

_____

_____

NOW SOME QUESTIONS ABOUT YOUR
USE OF MEDICAL SERVICES

16. During the past two
years, how many times
have you yourself had to
see a doctor?

____Haven't had to see a
doctor at all

____Once or twice a year

____Three or four times a
year

____Five times a year or
more

17. During the past two
years, how many times has
your wife or husband had
to see a doctor?

____Not married

____Hasn't had to see a
doctor at all

____Once or twice a year

____Three or four times a
year

____Five times a year or
more

18. During the past two
years, how many times
have your children had to
see a doctor?

____No children

____None of the children
have had to see a
doctor at all

____Children average once
or twice a year

____Children average three
or four times a year

____Children average five
times a year or more

19. Have you or your wife or
husband ever gone to a
second doctor to get his
opinion about some condi-
tion without telling your
first doctor about going?

____Yes, before I belonged
to HIP

____Yes, when I belonged
to HIP

____Yes, several times
before and while I
belonged to HIP

____No, never

20. Have you or your wife or
husband ever stopped
going to a doctor because
you weren't satisfied
with him?

____Yes, both a non-HIP
and a HIP doctor

____Yes, only a non-HIP
doctor

____Yes, only a HIP doctor

____No, never

21. During the past two
years, has any doctor
recommended some medicine
or treatment or operation
to you or your wife or
husband that you haven't
carried out?

____Yes, several times

____Yes, once or twice

____No, carried out all
recommendations

22. Did you or your wife or
husband ever have an ex-
perience with a doctor

when you felt you were
insulted?

____Yes, by both HIP and
non-HIP doctors

____Yes, by a HIP doctor
only

____Yes, by a non-HIP
doctor only

____No, never

23. Did you or your wife or
husband ever have a doc-
tor who seemed to be
incompetent?

____Yes, both HIP and non-
HIP doctors

____Yes, a HIP doctor only

____Yes, a non-HIP doctor
only

____No, never

THE NEXT FEW QUESTIONS ARE
ABOUT OPERATIONS AND
CHILDBIRTHS ONLY

24. During your adult life,
have you yourself ever
had a surgical operation
(or childbirth) requiring
hospitalization?

____Yes

____No

25. Have you or any member of
your family had an opera-
tion (or a baby de-
livered) by a HIP doctor?

____Yes

____No

26. Since you've been in HIP
have you or any member
of your family covered by
HIP had an operation (or
a baby delivered) by a
non-HIP doctor?

____Yes, at our own
expense

____Yes, expenses paid by
Blue Shield or some
other surgical plan to
which we also belong

____Yes, but HIP paid our
expenses

____No, never (Skip to
question 30)

27. If you answered "yes,"
check the family mem-
bers eligible for HIP
who had an operation
(or baby delivered) by a
non-HIP doctor.

____Husband

____Wife

____Children up to 6 years
old

____Children 6 years old
and over

28. If you answered "yes,"
please write in the
nature of the operation
and the reason for not
using a HIP doctor.

_____

_____

_____

29. If you answered "yes"
check the item that de-
scribes the non-HIP
doctor who performed the
operation or delivery.

____A doctor we knew
before joining HIP

____A doctor we didn't
know before joining
HIP

THE NEXT FEW QUESTIONS ARE
ABOUT ORDINARY MEDICAL CARE,
NOT OPERATIONS OR CHILD-
BIRTHS

30. Except for operations,
during the time you have
been in HIP, did you or
any member of your family
covered by HIP ever use
the services of a non-HIP
doctor?

____Yes, use a non-HIP
doctor for most medi-
cal needs, hardly
using HIP at all

____Yes, have used a non-
HIP doctor, but HIP
has been used for most
medical needs

____No, never used non-HIP
doctors while entitled
to HIP care (Skip to
question 34)

31. If you answered "yes,"
check the family members
eligible for HIP care who
have used non-HIP
doctors.

____Husband

____Wife

____Children up to 6 years
old

____Children 6 years old
and over

32. If you answered "yes,"
check the item that
describes the non-HIP
doctor you used the most.

____A doctor known before
joining HIP

____A doctor not known
before joining HIP

33. If you answered "yes"
check the ONE item below
that best describes your
major reason for not
using HIP doctors.

____Don't feel HIP doctors
are very good

____Couldn't get appoint-
ments at HIP

____Used to the non-HIP
doctors and didn't
want to try HIP
doctors

____Emergency

____Don't feel HIP doctors
are interested enough

____Other:_____
_____
_____
_____

NOW A FEW MORE QUESTIONS
ABOUT HIP

34. Do you feel your present
Family Doctor at HIP
takes as much interest in
you as he should?

____Yes

____No

____Never used him

35. If you have children, do
you feel your present HIP
pediatrician takes as
much interest in your
children as he should?

____Yes

____No

____Haven't used pediatri-
cian

36. Do you feel the HIP specialists you've seen take as much interest in you as they should?

____Haven't used any specialists

____Yes

____No

37. Are the nurses, receptionists, and phone operators at Montefiore on the whole courteous or are they hard to get along with?

____Most are courteous and pleasant

____Most are courteous and cold

____Most are rude and disagreeable

38. Some people say the Montefiore Group has a clinic atmosphere that makes them feel they're charity cases. Do you agree?

____Yes, very much

____Yes, a bit

____No, not at all

39. On the whole, are you satisfied with the care you've gotten at Montefiore?

____Yes, completely satisfied

____Some complaints but generally satisfied

____No, generally dissatisfied

40. Is your wife or husband satisfied with the Montefiore Medical Group?

____Not married or not covered by HIP

____Yes, completely satisfied

____Some complaints but generally satisfied

____No, generally dissatisfied

41. If you have friends who belong to HIP, what do they feel about the care they get?

____Most are completely satisfied

____Most have some complaints but are generally satisfied

____Most are generally dissatisfied

____About the same number satisfied as not

____Don't know what they think

FINALLY, A FEW MORE QUESTIONS ABOUT YOU

42. What is your major occupation?

_____

43. If a housewife, what was your former occupation?

_____

44. How much schooling have you had?

____No schooling

____Some grammar (elementary) school

____Graduated grammar school

____Some high school

____Graduated high school

____Some college

____Graduated college

____Postgraduate college work

45. In what country were you born?

_____

46. What is your national background?

____German–American

____Irish–American

____Italian–American

____Russian–American

____Some other country:____

_____

46. What is your religious background?

____Protestant

____Catholic

____Jewish

____None

____Another religion:_____

_____


THIS IS THE END OF THE QUESTIONNAIRE.   THANK YOU.
PLEASE MAIL BACK AS SOON AS POSSIBLE IN THE STAMPED
RETURN ENVELOPE.

# INDEX

# Index